PRENDERGAST'S FALL

PRENDERGAST'S FALL

BY
DAVID CAMERON

into books

First published in 2019 by Into Books.

ISBN 978-1-5272-4184-8

Into Books is an imprint of Into Creative, Glasgow, Scotland.
intocreative.co.uk

Typeset in Bembo.
Cover and page design by Stephen Cameron.

For my brother Stephen,
who gave me the bones of Prendergast.

'You'll have further to fall,' she said,
'If the life you have constructed
Doesn't fit who you are.' I said:

'Like Alice down the rabbit-hole,'
As if to glamorise the fall
And dodge the hardness of it all

– Although if distance has much sway
In how I'll land or who I'll be
I don't know, and she didn't say.

0

thou

dark

thou

light

ow!

into the

ow!

out of the

nothing

before ow!

all

after ow!

dark

ow! and ow!

light

ow! and ow!

1

In truth in lies in light in dark.

Dance to the daddy, sing to the mammy.

Like the eyes at the royal tombs of Ur.

Enter that vortex. In your prime a moment then it's gone.

The Empress and Death.

Only death is beauty's peer.

Hunched gnomishly on the branch.

In altarlight hear the traffic surf.

A world of dark.

The big moon up in the blue. The high rise on the horizon.

Everything arse-over-elbow.

Not here. Not now.

Salute them as they pass, finite now, filing like metal birds.

A different gravity, perhaps.

Why so strong in the beginning? And after the end?

Until now. Until then.

2

My Dad on the striped deckchair, a dog at his feet. Not our dog. I crawl onto his lap. He puts one hand above his eyes, like a soldier. I do it too. He smiles.

- The ceiling is safe, she says.

　　I'm not to worry about the crack.

　　My hand touches the bump on her forehead.

　　- A mole, she says.

　　I'm not to worry about the mole.

　　She's safe.

- He'll get piles sitting there.

　　I make my hand a star for it to go on.

　　The red spider.

Dad's single in my hands. Hold it by its edge, like he says. The green apple one side, the halved apple the other. The halved apple doesn't go brown. Cut an apple the other way you see a star, like he showed me. That one did.

Next-door Alison at the sink with me. Who can make the

most bubbles from soap? My game. I have the dark-green Fairy for dishes, so I lose. I'm not sad to lose, she is laughing so much. I have made her happy.

Watch with Mother.

The lid of the twin tub propped against the wall. In the living room out of sight. Just the corner of the machine in the rope-held mirror. Above the mantelpiece. Hear the washing being slopped with the wooden tongs. There's time.

Raise a wind in my head, and it happens, it always does.

I float. Above the lid.

Till the spinner stops. Last whimper like a dog's.

I help spread the pink over the glass. It's all she lets me help her with.

Windowlene like Calamine Lotion. The dirty duster to spread, the clean duster to wipe.

Long strips of wood with screws. The windows hanging off, on bits of rope.

Wide open to the world. What world there is.

Funny to feel invisible when wholly seen, visible when partly.

She won't look at me.

A red ball rolls between the feet. My red ball, not my feet.

We are upstairs. The bus is moving.

– Don't move, she says.

I see the ball roll out of sight. I hear it roll, not out of hearing.

Stop at a light. I make a dash for it.

My ball again. My good red ball.

Sit back down without looking. I know what her look will be.

Then tap.

– I think your mum is back there.

The shock of a wrong mum. The bigger shock of wanting to stay with her.

And lemons and St Clement's. Left me in the middle of the floor with my Kidditunes records. Song after song I put on. Fun and joy for girl and boy.

Want the song to end when it starts. Wish the song had never ended when it ends. The song in the middle, where is it?

Fun and joy.

Use any needle.

I get to pull the tartan trolley which is my train. There but not back again. Back it's full of messages.

The gaps between the slabs make the noise of the train. Some of the slabs are cracked, like ceilings.

She stops to speak. Yes, she has her helper with her today. She smiles. Not a real smile.

Bulloch's for what she forgot in the Co. Then the other Co, the butcher's. She tells him our number. Three double five nine five.

Then either the newsagents or Manhattan Cafe which isn't a cafe for their cigarettes. Twenty Embassy tipped for her, twenty Regal for Dad.

The train is too heavy, even before we get to Greggs.

A loaf, two Paris buns and a fern cake.

Light like a black Tunnock teacake on its side. I could reach the switch. On the chair, I could reach the switch. The doctor wouldn't like it.

How many more to go? We were here before her.

- Don't stare, Mum says.

How can I not stare? Half of her face is purple.

- Is that beetroot juice?

- Shh!

Won't even let me swing my legs under the chair.

Awful is Mum's word for hellish. Hellish is dad's word. This is hellish.

Flick the switch.

The swing still swinging long after I leave it.

I'm not allowed down the chute. There is mess on it, she says.

The frying pan too dangerous. Only the roundabout's left.

I want back on the swing, I can see Dad's work from there. The roof like the dark paper on top of Mum's chocolates.

He is inside with the aeroplane engines. What does he do to them?

Black Magic.

She has too many pillows. The bed is too high.

- That's put paid to that, then, Mum says.

- Don't, Dad says.

He is stroking her bare arm.

They think that saying Mum isn't well is enough. They think that not well is all I understand.

She's had a hysterectomy. I know how to say it, I'm not a baby.

She puts her head into one. Like a beehive that's open. All with curlers in. Six in a row. Magazines on laps. I would like to crawl onto hers. Because of the noise and. Odd that we're in a house.

This blonde woman is always being nice to me. Gives me crayons and a pad of paper. The pad is nearly full already. I don't know what to do to it.

Mum keeps glancing over. Smiles when I see. Not real smiles.

Don't worry, Mum. You're safe.

– You haven't been up all night?

Dad rubs his chin, smiles.

– Not all night.

He is switching on the television set. In the morning!

I like their window. A window like that in my room would be good. Like half a star, not round or square or arched. To watch the moon through.

3

Mum said not to cry. Why would I cry?

    If they cry, will I? Will they laugh if I cry?

    I might cry, I might. Mum cries at night.

    Why would I cry?

Miss says g is gi when g is ji. R–o–g–e–r. It's on our door.

    What else doesn't she know?

It's called a sandpit. They act like they've seen one before.

    That girl is laughing, wiggling her toes in the sand. I don't think we are supposed to take our shoes off.

    She has sand on her hand. She runs her sandy hand through her blonde hair.

    I feel funny.

Carry it on at playtime. One shove deserves another.

    - Fight! Fight!

    Most alive I've ever been. Then the bell goes.

    - I won it, didn't I?

    - I don't think so.

    - No, I did, I won it.

- I think he did.

- Shut up.

- Where, oh where is dear little Martin?

Where, oh where is dear little Martin?

Where, oh where is dear little Martin?

Way down yonder in the paw-paw patch.

Come on girls, let's go find him,

Come on girls, let's go find him,

Come on girls, let's go find him,

Way down yonder in the paw-paw patch.

Nothing left to read in the infants' store cupboard. Takes me upstairs.

Smell of stacks of new books. Shows me one book, then another, then another.

- That one.

- That one's a bit scary-looking.

- I want it.

Creatures on the front, godlike or like sea devils. A man wrestling with a beast on the back. Or beast with a beastlier beast.

No other book could ever touch this one. Whatever words are in it.

Brave and Bold. The Book of Gold.

Talk about a tandem. Mum giving up halfway round the island, Dad propelling them both. Laughter and tears. Of laughter, Dad says.

Talk about a time, any time, before me. They love it.

They act as if I didn't know she's dead. They put me in her room, as if I didn't know she's dead. Her dresses are inside the wardrobe, still. I know they are.

Just for the one night, they said.

Check my pillow for white hairs. The sheets, the blankets.

Uncle's voice a deeper rumbling than Dad's. Aunt's abrupt laugh.

Mum will come in to soothe me if I cry. She's listening, hoping I will, I know she is.

Not. One. Sound.

In the box room that was his dark room once upon a time.

Singing in the mirror, tape recorder at my feet, as near as the lead stretches.

The yellow label, A Collection of Beatles Oldies (But Goldies!).

Trying to persuade me that she loves me. Listening to tell the voices apart.

Smooth or rasp, which am I?

I thought I was smooth. Once upon a time.

I rasp.

In the green glen. Via the secret path. A walking stick soon found. Miniature version for me. Glancing up at him. Glancing up through the trees. My sky-father.

The talk goes all ways. Ends at a five-pointed star. Draws it in the dirt with his stick. I haven't ventured beyond the six-pointed. An upside-down triangle on a triangle is easy.

– A good attempt, he says.

Never failed in his eyes.

Close them, Dad.

A Hunter to a Thoroughgood. Miss, that can't be right.

Stay as you are. It must be better to be a Hunter. And though you always tell us to be good, nobody should be Thoroughgood.

I'll miss you, Miss. When you come back most of all.

No more a Hunter.

A bit higher each time. Till I take my hands off my thighs completely. Stand upright, with only head bowed. Leap over that, frog. My neck for the chop if he doesn't.

He does, and we laugh. Branny, who never saw much in me before. Said as much.

Showaddywaddy and dinosaurs. I could learn to like them.

Dreepie in the lock-ups. Hanging on for dear life. Edging along a bit further each time. The car park sloping so the fall longer each time. Is longer right? Deeper, fuller. The landing harder each time. Jolt to the head. A pain like too much ice cream at once, only worse. Each time it is worse. But able to. Until we move to the diseased elm. Leap from a bit higher each time. The branches thinner each time. Thinner is right. The leap harder each time. Until I can't do it any more. The branch they leapt from. And below, baying. Barking, braying. Kerry and Branny. I can't do it. Any more.

Red sky at night, shepherd's delight. Red sky in the morning, shepherd's warning.

Branny says sailor's.

I might change it to sailor's. After tonight.

The shepherd helps me sleep.

My friend of only weeks brought low. His face a foot above the dirt. Buchan clutching the roots of his hair. Didn't manage to get a single swing at him before. And it goes on, it still goes on. We were baying for blood, now we want it to stop, just stop. Or I do. My kingly friend brought low. His purple face a foot above the dirt. Buchan kicking it.

Panicking, insert the pencil to respool the tape. But the tape is twisted. Break Dad's taboo, use thumb and forefinger to flatten it. The sound will doubtless be dull at those points, but mustn't let the tape snap.

The tape snaps. This is the end of everything. Z Cars, Dr Who, The Avengers, Catweazle, Captain Scarlet. All the tunes are gone.

How can I face her? Probably thinking already, I should never have let him take it home. Amazed she did. Nothing ever linked home and school before. To feel the same fear hearing the Dr Who tune in class as I do in the house. Fear is the glue.

And now the fear of her face when I tell her.

Get Mum and Dad to buy a new one, but they won't. They'll think it enough to explain.

It isn't enough to explain, why can't they see that?

4

As if the cars are thirsty. The queue snaking out the garage, onto Maxwellton Road.

I like the haze.

Dad with his sleeves rolled up, white work shirt, pen still in pocket, elbow propped.

All windows rolled down, even mine.

I like the smell.

- Idiots need to switch their engines off.

Devise a general law from this. All those who, in stationary cars, leave their engines running are idiots.

The world makes sense, and smells good.

I'm so glad to be alive.

That isn't plasticine. Shit on the floor! Under our desks!

Cylindrical and thin shit.

We have never been so outraged or so happy. Shit on the floor!

Mrs Woods oddly not. The pointing finger of shame is ours not hers.

Bernadette Stapleton.

How did she get it there? That's the wonder.

Papier-mâché puppets of dream. Arts and craftsy Mrs Woods will show us.

- You should be good at this, she says.

I should be, but I'm not. I like to draw. With a 2B pencil, a crisp new sheet of drawing paper.

Wallpaper paste and chicken wire. The stuff of nightmares. Slop everything on and wait.

The knife sticking into the skull I say's a ponytail.

- All right.

I've seen that look before.

The tomboy of the team, just as good as any of us. Like Jinky on the wing. But Mr McCourt won't let her go. Across the road to the rugby pitch nobody plays on. Rugby least of all. Out of school bounds. The boys can go, not the tomboy. But she's just as good as any of us, I say. We all say. Each excepting himself, of course. Silently.

Eyes. It's always the eyes. Not a boy's eyes.

Resolve not to go if she can't. We all do. Stick to the playground. The hard tarmac, a stone for a ball. When we could have a Mitre ball, spongy grass, goalposts.

One peels off, two peel off, three. To the rugby pitch nobody plays on. Rugby least of all.

It will be good for her to play with the other girls, they might start to like her.

Always the eyes.

Keeping score with the pencils we use for Cluedo. Just this gives me butterflies.

Have to work it so that Miss United Kingdom comes

out on top. Mum on for her too. Dad never is. Says Miss South Africa will win it, though she should be a coloured woman. What sense does that make?

Now it's the swimsuit round.

– Do you need your pencil sharpened, dear?

It's not that funny.

Flinches at my drawing of a trepanned skull. She thinks I don't see her do it, but I do. She will put her hand to her throat in a minute. Less than.

I mention Hippocrates.

– You say Hippocrates, she says.

We don't believe in demons any more. I am not to spend so much time on the ancients. Something more up-to-date. The creation of the National Health Service, for instance.

Feel my skull where the bore-hole would be. Yes, would be good to have it there.

Aim for the railing.

She shouts up. The woman disappears and reappears. Her mum, clearly. But not to lead the girl inside.

We are standing behind her in a ring. That moves back when she moves towards. Nobody passes by.

Words we all want to shout at our mums too, sometimes.

We look at each other wild-eyed. Or her eyes are wild. Not hers, hers. Mhairi's.

– She has fits, she says.

See again the photo in the paper. Gun-toting Patty Hearst.

Nothing happens. The girl shouts up. The woman

moves across the glass.

God is evil.

Mhairi my blonde Valentine. Reciprocated this year.

They line up with theirs. I keep mine hidden.

Mrs Woods asks to see. Teachers don't ask, really.

What others say, I don't give a damn. And there'll be a baby in that pram.

Puts a hand over her mouth. I know what she is doing.

– You gave Martin one too?

– Why is that so strange?

Love this about her. Unafraid to stand up to them. I keep mine hidden.

– Well, you are so friendly and outgoing, and.

Incomplete, but still hurts. Carry my hurt with me to the TV room, which is the dinner-room stage with the curtain closed. Rainbow on, for some reason. We aren't infants.

Squats on the dusty black floor beside me. Propped, each, by our far arm.

Our free hands find each other.

Something afoot. In the blue bus shelter with Mum, waiting for a red bus. The 181. Graffiti scratched into the plastic glass. Told by her not to read it. Somebody ending in a is a cocksucker.

Eventually the tenements, like sea-devils in the mist.

Up the clean steps, three storeys, count them.

The door opens wide, her smile is wide.

– Mary. Martin.

See them hug, as never before. Together or apart.

No need to breathe a word to Dad. Aunt not a Prendergast, I do understand that.

Talk about baby blues confuses. I'm not one and she doesn't have one.

– You married the better brother, Mary.

If my uncle and my aunt divorced, then my dad and my mum could.

They wouldn't.

Why is she being so nice to her? Hardly seeing me.

I know where the Luger is kept.

The fight in the night. Ali and a man in a leopard-skin hat, walking at a strange pace. My hero and Dad's hero. Not fair that his crown will be decided in my sleep. Wish I was one of those boys play-fighting in the dirt. Smiling with fists raised. Confusing as unlike the Black Babies we give our pennies to. Black-and-white photos of black children who aren't babies. Why are their bellies so fat if they're so hungry? Flies. Fly like a butterfly. How good would it be to be the champion of the world? They say that too for other weights, but it doesn't count. Up to ten. Down to ten for a rocket. Ali in space, the champion of the universe. The man in the hat not smiling.

Our last tryst. Tryst the wrong word. Along the gravel path. Gravel the wrong word.

McElhinney there too. We find a tree. A willow, I see it now. Balsa, we say.

Balsa! Hack it out with our hands.

Just as the SRA Reading Lab card said it would be. Light, light as anything, lighter than any wood there ever was.

Drag it home. To our different homes. His home that won't be there any more.

That will be in Shetland, with the ponies.

Always was the adventurous Martin.

Too consumed with passion for the balsa to pay heed to sorrow. Drag it home, out the back, to sculpt it with Dad's tools. When he gets home from work. When he gets home from work he says, This is dead wood, son.

Goodbye, friend.

- Uh-huh, assassination, that's what you need.

Clark starts it. Buchan picks it up.

We smile, embarrassed. Deep down we are good boys.

The Record Breakers minus the ashen-skinned McWhirter twins. Minus one of them. Anything that interferes with our relaxed calm at teatime not funny.

Not that we protest. Smile without laughter the height of it.

Hot day. The queue snaking out the door. At the drinking fountain, V-shaped sink with stubby water-spout, boys who'd run their chests sore in the playground ape and bob but keep in line, obedient to the prefect. Who sits by the sink in a broken chair, gleefully metering the water. Counting to ten, now slowly, now quickly, so that the youngest gets least, his pals their fill.

I swell with rage.

To a small crowd that listens meekly I promise that, when my time comes, every boy will be allotted the exact-same amount of water: enough to slake his thirst.

Sitting here now, by the same sink, a prefect, fed up with the noise, the stench of piss, I count over a small boy's head.

- Onetwothreefourfivesixseveneight

Don't get further till I recall. A hot day, the queue snaking out the door.

My younger thirst. For justice. In this very place.

Telling a joke at playtime. A Billy Connolly LP in the neighbours' house. Long, longer when I tell it. Not good at jokes but committed this one to memory. Blush surging as it goes on, till I don't know if laughing at me or the joke. Had to do it, though. Couldn't go through life unable to tell a joke. Typical to choose the longest one. Only ever rated Becher's Brook in the National. Not easy on myself. Not easy on other people. Murder in the mirror. To win, never each way.

On my jotter, a swastika. Made from the L in the top right-hand corner. Have been doing this undetected for a year at least. Only one to choose the Axis Forces in the war project. She praised me for that. Swim against the tide, son, Dad says. Or only dead fish swim with the tide. Depending on his mood.

- Martin Prendergast!

She sees it now. Demands an explanation, her words.

- That way round it's an Indian symbol, Miss.

- Don't insult my intelligence.

Have to cover it up, she says. I go back to my desk, turn the legs into feathers. This isn't good enough, apparently. I must cover the jotter at home with brown paper or wallpaper. The roll of woodchip in the cupboard under the stairs.

The cupboard under the stairs! Same dark in me as the swastika does. Is that wrong?

Dad on the beach on a cold July day. Hands in pockets, nudging pebbles with his foot.

- You still wish we'd gone to Blackpool instead?

Keep my head bowed. Once something a certainty, ungenerous to complain. He taught me that.

- This is real nature, son. A man-made tower can't compete with this.

Too ashamed to tell him it's the rollercoaster not the tower. Brogan almost died on it it was so good.

- Smell the sea.

I smell the sea. Never did like fishy smells.

- This is the life, I say.

He smiles. The universe smiles.

5

He leans against the mantelpiece, in the centre where the clock is. Heartburn, I'll have to get him a glass of milk in a minute. Becoming more frequent now.

The Kraken Wakes. I have just been telling him about it, the aliens' sea tanks, the sea levels rising. Tapping my right foot, putting off going to the toilet. I look up. He is looking down. He places his forehead on the mantelpiece, to the left of the clock. It is like a game. I don't know the rules. He has always been good at explaining the rules of games. He has always been a patient reader of the rules of games.

He is thrown back. One leg crossed over the other on the mat.

– Jesus Christ, Dad.

Mum runs in from the kitchen, screams. A scream like an animal's. I'll not forget.

A raised arm. A limp arm in space.

What do I do? What do I do now?

She sidles up to me. No, not so. Suddenly she is at my side.

A mass of molten features.

– Pray to your dad in an emergency and he will grant

your wishes. Not to God, don't listen to what they say. To your dad.

Shuffles off, a fat, black widow spider.

That can't be right, can it?

I feel the blood drain from my face. Odd to be nervous going up on the altar. On such an occasion. The congregation like a wall.

A reading from the prophet Isaiah.

My mouth clicks, into the microphone.

Should you pass through the sea, I will be with you. The sea at Rothesay, at Gourock, at Dunoon. Holding the rod steady in my hands.

We lost a lot of weights that day.

Mum in her veil alarming. Didn't think it possible any more. Benedictus qui venit in nomine Domini. Some things you don't forget.

From the pier we caught nothing again.

I will be exactly as I am now for the rest of my life.

Should you walk through fire.

Encased in yellow or pink icing, the lace doilies under. Paper lace.

They are all here. Uncle with his new German wife, with his first wife hovering at their edges. Making sudden darting movements.

- I had to pay my respects. I know Roger didn't want you two seeing me.

- Hush, Mum says. The word hush.

People in clusters, laughing, cutting short their laughter. Cut-short laughter is the order of the day.

I am what I see, what I hear. The other senses don't matter.

The priest is the first to leave. Makes a quick bow. He didn't know Dad from Adam.

The free bar at an end soon. Last orders.

Last words. His life distilled.

They are all gone away.

The long hot. A sprinkler ban, apparently. Some people have sprinklers, apparently.

This is the One O'Clock News. This is the Six O'Clock News. This is the Nine O'Clock News.

This is the News at Ten, with Reginald Bosanquet.

I hear her, moving in her sleep.

Nothing worse than a child dying before you, I've heard her say. And a child going to bed after you?

The same cracks in the ceiling still worrying me.

If their bed falls through.

I still say their.

New school a new world. Different smells, first day smells. No polished wood, mopped linoluem. No pristine plasticine, nothing of anything like that.

A woman with her hair tied tight, a black swirl from the back. Enter that vortex. If I only could.

She is greeting us breezily. What did we do in the holidays?

– Anyone?

Please, God, let her not ask me. Please, God.

She asks me.

- My dad died in the holidays, Miss.

She turns her back on the class. Lifts her hand to her face.

I know what she is doing.

Two Man Hunt, as in the old days. Run, run, as fast as we can. Across the main road, through a close. Shimmering blue walls, door slam echoes. Out onto the back green. Except the body gives up. Suddenly, unexpectedly. Just. Gives up.

- You run on.

Might as well get caught, join the hunters. Excuse slow running as thinking.

I am thinking.

What just happened there?

Shivering in the dinner queue, McCafferty.

- This is the best bit, not eating the chips, thinking about eating them.

I look at his mouth.

It's true.

Why can't the best bit be eating the chips? Why?

- You can't go inside unless it's raining.

But it is, it was. See, the playground's wet. The drains are still gurgling. If you go inside when it's raining you'll get two of the belt. I won't because I'll say no. Say no, then. I just did. And? His face red as a fucking lobster. He doesn't know what to do. Instead an essay on the necessity of corporal punishment. I can do that. Add or otherwise after necessity and I can do that. Tear him to shreds. Before he tears it to shreds. He's not my dad.

I went inside when it wasn't raining and am here to tell the tale.

Tell it.

The Woody at it again. Even more riveting. Mum leads the way to their room to watch. Still say their.

Two girls fighting.

· – Look at them! Girls are much worse than boys.

Not in fact allowed to look in case they see. Hear the screams and the curses. Picture it all. Beowulf grappling with Grendel on the back of Brave and Bold. In high heels and skirts.

Now a man's voice. Deep, rumbling. Mr Suds.

Everything all right suddenly.

Look out when alone. The tree, the orange streetlight. Death again.

He has a huge head. His huge head is bent over buttons. Teaches them tactility, the woman says. He isn't touching anything, I want to say.

We file past. We are very used to filing past.

A woman with a withered arm, whiskers on her chin, babbling. Something about bramble jam.

– There but for the Grace of God, boys.

And out the door we trot.

I don't believe that.

I see the two faces. And I see the parallel lines.

Mystical feeling from that vase.

Periodic table the Ten Commandments. The curved tap a veiled acolyte. Ask me why.

Among the optical illusions a stretched chequerboard. See again the woman sprawled over one. Dark-haired, neck veins visible. Anatomy for the Artist, smuggled that one in. Cause to be grateful to her on many a night. Too many, doesn't do it for me now.

Leave it a bit and she will.

Guitar like a coffin. Carry it in. Lay it down.

Folk mass preparation. Meet in a room with soft chairs. Soft, electric blue chairs. This is a place apart.

And she is there, large as life, larger than she was. My blonde Valentine.

Only performed solo before. Or audience Mum, out of earshot if possible. Might be good.

They strum and immediately I see I am not. Playing barre chords. What are barre chords?

She the best of all. Always was perfect.

Could cope without applause. Never thought I'd be no good though.

Has an ingrown toenail, she says. Not to me. We don't talk any more. When we did we didn't much. Held hands in the dark.

A pile of crap anyway. Imagine without the no heaven.

Diminished, diminishing.

I won't be doing that again.

On the rampage again. Tearing up the tree roots, or trying to. The exposed veins.

The Crazy Woody. Sprayed on the chute in the swing

park.

Mum behind the blinds, twitching them. Lights off so they won't see. They will see the lights going off.

A new chant tonight.

- The workers united will never be divided.

- Morons, she says. They don't even know the right word.

- What is the right word?

- Defeated, she says, defeated.

Refuge in the smell of linseed oil. The corner room letting precious light in. No desk for Miss, she prefers it that way. Young, if teachers can be young, dark-haired. Think she was in that jungle painting above the neighbour's fireplace. Warm comfort. Yet exacting.

Everyone else monkeying around. Patience makes me better. Take the whole time to sketch a head the size of a coin's. She marvels at the detail.

Is the devil there? I am the devil so.

Quite a virtuous one. For my queen.

- You probably don't even know what a jock-strap is.

Merciless eating his chips. Whole table in earshot turns. This is the moment I've been preparing for.

The Concise Oxford English Dictionary my companion. Every dirty word in the book.

- It's a support for male genitals.

- I'm impressed, Prendy.

Turns his head to the girl beside him. One of the tough girls, always alluring.

And that should be it. Inquisition over. Till I drive the point home.

- It helps to keep it up during intercourse.

The head swivels back. Mad-dog sneer.

She the first to laugh.

A dictionary is not enough.

6

In all my dreams, before my helpless sight.

Never really paid attention before. Never thought much of any of it before.

Poets devisers of crossword puzzles. Cryptic, at that.

Even said it. If someone has something to say, let him say it clearly.

He plunges at me. Only, I want to say towards.

In my dreams, it's towards. Always.

The Poky Hall in daylight. Block it out with posters but it gets through.

She is here, dancing. Almost never stops. Stopped once when asked, I noticed that.

In my bleached-white jeans that still reek of bleach. Much, much younger than she. Two, three years.

Green Onions comes on. Well, now or never.

- Do you want to dance?

Smile or smirk, it doesn't matter, she's still here.

Launch into it, while she.

Toes left, heels left. Toes right, heel right. Barely call it movement.

The discrepancy between our styles alarming.

Still, grateful. Then and always.

In step up the broad staircase. Hannigan, I've seen him before. Turns the gas tap on in Science till we can't stand it. Dark, brooding face. Goes out with a girl with big hair.

Dream talk. I tell him mine about Martin.

- When he comes back, everything feels right again.

- Your dad died a couple of years back, right?

- Right. So what?

- Martin's in place of your dad, in the dream.

Feel the hairs on my arms stir.

- Right.

Part at the top.

I think we could be friends.

Tears all around. Rome, the eternal city. A day and a night and a day to get here. The laugh, some squalid quarter. I feel like laughing. The girls I desire and the girls I don't in tears, for the most part. One boy in tears, even. Teachers worriedly stern. The dormitory they hadn't anticipated. Or, the biggest laugh, the glass-walled toilets.

In the courtyard in the dark, Our Lady. A story about a statue moving. The White Lady down the glen.

Crying again, tears again.

Lie, one side of my face on the scratchy blanket, looking out of the window. Picturing Green Goddess fire engines, for some reason. Mum at home, relieved, I don't doubt it. In the dark too, perhaps.

Unmoving.

Jukebox in the Italian mountains. We are permitted to. Syrupy drinks. The lire makes no sense to us.

Everything makeshift. Doled out to the natives like evacuees. Evacuated from Rome, the eternal city. Landed the richest woman too. Warm water in her bathroom suite only. Bucket of cold out the back for us.

– Have you noticed something?

– What?

– No girls.

And then all that changes. The Sunday church-bell drawing them out, like a bread poultice. Girls in black. Uniformly lovely.

A heaven worth waiting for.

– No, you're the idiot.

As in a dream or TV show, class quiet as I say it. Just at the moment that I say it. Whisper it, so I think. Anger doesn't whisper.

– Come up here!

Doesn't even ask to explain.

And would say what? My dad was a union man? Slate them, you slate him? My dad a better man than.

You have to be joking. He's actually doing it, unbending the belt.

– I haven't taken this out in thirteen years.

Last time refused. Too stunned to now.

Any tears involuntary, incipient.

Ha! He'd enjoy the Latin.

Refrain. Each night she cries herself softly to sleep.

Hesitate to post. Running out of poems to send, only

this first left. Weird to send one about Mum. To her.

A drawing would give the game away.

Whole thing weird. Feel like a stalker. That play for today. He's in the house!

She's in the phone book, after all. No, her dad, it's always the dad. For us too.

Us two.

And splashed in the paper. Her place in the Royal Ballet School. Fairytale ending. Fairytale beginning. Will always remember the way she danced. That day. It was day. With me. If I remember anything.

She has been telling all. All her pals. Even I heard, innocently. The poems through the post. One more, make it the last.

And laughing. And laughing.

Genius, he said.

At last. Said at last. Somebody said it at last.

– They aren't used to having bright pupils in Economics.

Well, that's true. But so like her to take me down a peg.

– He has something planned for you, she says.

All stems from my essay on Marx. My choice. Took me to task for it, but could tell impressed. Had I actually read Das Kapital? No, only the Communist Manifesto. Soviet edition. White, with miniature hammer and sickle.

– What?

She explains as if explaining a treat. When it's only pocket money for chores.

Wants me acquisitive. Get capitalism into my bones. Unmarx me.

My hand a fist. He's not my dad.

Unseal the tupperware and whole room groans.

- Egg and onion?

- Yip.

Chalked on the blackboard of the packed lunch room. Communism: an economic and social system based on the common ownership of the means of production. Down on the tractor farm.

Smile to Hannigan. Mere mention an affirmation. Exists in the world.

- I hate that sort of clever-clever.

Impresses that he feels things strongly. Whereas more like a loose signpost in the wind. This, no this, no this.

And I am that now.

Legs & Co. Never saw the point, really. Pointless dancing. Who would watch that, given the choice?

There's a point now. There's a chance now. Some sort of flailing of limbs to effect a change. Slow if not stop me. Find another beanstalk, Jack. Brother Jack. Sleeping through your non-existence. I would climb. Would I climb? Has it come to this? Too soon for regret. Another millisecond maybe. The old vertigo.

A man singing stop crying. Voice of a man not boy. Imagine me that, when I am that. Only, not then. Crawl down to the river babe. Say that, you get a slap.

Search the faces of the dancers. Must be something there. Hurt that can't be covered up.

What is the part of woman not her legs? Company?

Shepherded to the church. Outside the school gate even, like traffic police. No escape this time. In the redbrick cave with the alcoves. Christened here, once upon a time. My dad in attendance behind the lens. Sacred to me, in spite of all. Would spit in the font for effect now, to prove unbelief. Frighten the sheep. The good little sheep.

Who aren't in heaven, hollow be thy name. Clever of me.

One tuts. Nobody laughs.

I hear her. In her bedroom.

She thinks I'm downstairs. Carpeted stairs, easy to creep up them. The door warped, never closes.

'Don't get me wrong, I love him, I just. Don't like him right now.'

Was there even a right now? Do I soothe myself?

At least I solved the question, How much contempt can she take? Less than I can show. That's good to know.

The woods near Anne Livie's house. Just us and a glue-sniffer. Hannigan listening. Don't know what's got into me today.

– I want to be buried there, above the burn.

It's a good spot, a hump like a grave already. No headstone, nothing to mark it.

– What would it say if you did have one?

– I Am Not Going to Cry Out Any More.

– That's good.

– What about yours?

– Don't know.

– Teresa's?

– Do You Want Anything from the Shops?

Love Will Tear Us Apart, again and again on the turntable.

The Trilogy in her room. Fags and Fine Fare Yellow Label coffee. Discussing the word hermaphrodite.

Abominable or Abominal Snowman? Said often enough, each wrong.

– But you looked good in a pork-pie hat.

We are all over the place. In the same place.

Eventually resolves itself into a snog. I with my head in the cupboard while they do.

Leaving, a sidelong look from Teresa.

I never know where I am.

In the room of bad smells. She with her plastic goggles on. Her white coat.

Experiment on the living, not the dead. See how much of anything they can take.

Bunsen burner at a tilt. The blue or the yellow or the red the hottest?

At the edge of our seats for this. Catalysis a process. Whereby.

The end product a cloudy gloop. A spurt of cum in the palm.

– What does that remind you of? Brogan asks.

The boys laugh and, after a bit, the girls laugh too. Laughing so hard the redness not taken for blush.

The tip of the inner blue.

Under the dragon tree, pleasantly. Effects wearing off now. Hannigan returning, jamjar in hand. Swirling the remnants around.

Look through the branches at the blue. No, look at the branches despite the blue.

One small moment of eternity.

Just as he said it would be.

7

Difficulties by the burn. Home in on them, on me. As if in a light aircraft. Get wings on my gravestone perhaps.

Too soon.

Kerr holding high my school bag. Kerry for short.

My disciple almost. Take him for granted, perhaps. Disciples do get taken for granted, perhaps.

Only now discerning weakness in me. Am starting to forget things. For instance, this bag. But not today.

A few landings on the banks of the burn first. Then smack dab in the middle.

Laughter like a hyena's. A fake hyena.

Round on him now, if one can round on. I can. So many years, so many selves. Every small grievance. Even to his ridiculous turn-ups aged, what? Eight?

The air not exactly cleared. Thick with shrapnel and debris.

Inhale the distress.

One pleated skirt after another. Racks of identical pleated skirts. She is drawn to the navy blue. Or is it royal? I am losing ground. Looks at me guiltily. Shouldn't be putting a boy through this, her look says. Not one his age. Indeterminable at speed. I have a sleepy feeling. Brain spongified. Feigning sharpness, trying, really trying to show interest. More than that, make interest genuine. Against whatever the expected thing is. The expected thing is sulk. Holds one against herself. What I think? I think it suits her. I do? I do. I am gaining ground.

Can we please leave?

Councillor stumbling over his words. Pupils to the right of him, parents to the left. Marry the two with prizes. Everybody loves prizes.

Mine only a joint one. Mum's face not so lit-up when she saw that. One of two. Couldn't soar off on my own, no. Not what life wants for me.

Hand them over, councillor. Mine John Donne: The Complete English Poems. Odd for an economics prize. Chose it myself, from Bell, Book and Candle, where Hannigan gets his incense. The smell of dope.

Liked the look of Donne, arms crossed, dark embroidered clothes like Jimmy Page's, hat and averted look. The man for me.

On stage, forget how to walk. Applause not lasting till I'm off it. Look at the book on way back. Head down, blush less visible.

Stay in my seat for God Save the Queen.

They'll be raging.

A bus through Europe in the dark. Only my second foreign holiday. No, third. Numbers so difficult. Wine at my feet, bought for Hannigan's dad. Ostensibly mum too, but it's the dad I have in mind. Two bottles, clinking at bends. They go through a bottle a night. At least. For two nights he will have me in mind. If he gives me a second.

Position feet to cushion bottles.

Sleepy.

Voices, my shoulder awake.

– What?

– At your feet.

Enough overhead light to see. The red spread.

Science and romance, in the Old Building. At least the priest isn't going round with a ruler, saying, You have to be this far apart. 30cm, the measure of distance between us.

Science does the best discos, that's what everybody says.

Enlightenment in the dark.

Have a good feeling tonight. Hannigan's joint helped with that. Didn't have our breath smelt on the way in. Though even Modern Languages doesn't bar you for fag-breath. Alcohol only. The one substance they abuse.

Not much in it for Hannigan. Can't very well cheat in open view. Get a bit stoned and ignore her. Make up later.

I'm a free man. Tonight I am.

On the floor for Tainted Love.

– You're a good dancer.

– Thanks. So are you.

Thanks with a kiss. More prolonged than any before.

– Did she have her tongue in your mouth?

Hannigan not happy. I am.

– Yes.

– You'll be getting her pregnant next.

Walks off, Teresa-wards. I don't need them tonight.

Clear view of the stars from the mouth of the underpass.

Tonight about mouths.

- This is a great poem, if any of you care about great poetry, if any of you are able to discern greatness in a poem.

Prick up my ears. Like the sound of greatness. Not usual to see him this animated.

Doleful man, he had it in for me from the start. This is a test.

- Oh Galuppi, Baldassaro.

Must be a mathematical formula for greatness. Fifteen three-lined verses. Eight stresses per line. That's 360 stresses. 360 degrees, a complete circle.

- Which is the best verse? Anyone?

This is a test.

Has to be the one with death stepped tacitly.

Say so.

- No.

The verse with dialogue, he says. *Were you happy? – Yes.*

I will go home, replicate the Browning. Now that I know the formula. Then he will have to see the greatness. In me.

Hark.

The Cow Goes Heuch. Imagine them coming up with that name. Someone must have laughed. Not so funny now with the lights on them. Turn their backs to the crowd.

A drama teacher the compère. It isn't Earl's Court, boys.

Hannigan in the mix, seems not to want to. Carrying high his Pepsi. Clever, put anything in, the black will hide it. Not eager to share. Stand here as if not alone.

No sign of Teresa tonight. Is that why he's looking

so relaxed?

Are they still tuning up?

Words eventually.

- Overseas to Calais sands, no impression, no demands.

Drift towards the illuminated exit. Not really a crowds person.

Good to know, I suppose.

Hate to see her cry. Any she.

But she, a blow to The Trilogy.

Has to be Hannigan. Going through one of his cruel phases. Look out.

- Teresa.

Palm flat on the lime-green wall she leans into. Upright, she curved. Supportive posture or towering over. Never know where I am with her.

- Don't cry.

- Martin.

Wet lashes, pleading eyes. They could be pleading.

Place a comforting hand. The grey of her sleeve, unravelling a little at the cuff, that's wet too.

- Why are you looking there?

Turns, not towards.

Looking where? Rewind to see.

A small stain, likely egg, below the V-neck.

The end of the affair.

His letters to his brother. There, in black and white. Explaining a world of colour. Intensest of yellows. Deliberate. He deliberated. Van Gogh's doing. Nothing to do with Dr Gachet.

Everything to do with drugs for Hannigan these days. Macbeth about magic mushrooms. I can't stand it.

And now the proof.

Sunflowers that way because he wanted them that way. Not digitalis, Dr Gachet's foxgloves.

He lies.

– You're a liar.

– I'm what?

– You're a liar.

– I'm a liar.

– Yes.

– Right.

And he goes. In the direction of the dragon tree.

Is this final? It feels it.

The haze a swarm of esses.

To my eyes.

Little pointed beard. Little pointed artist.

Are art teachers artists? Still?

Handy for him he has a walk-in cupboard. Not for materials only, Sir, is it? Your breath-altering cupboard.

See, he disappears. Into it.

I bet it's Teachers too. Only one way to.

– What the hell are you doing?

Swig it back, right in front of him.

– It will be our secret, Sir.

Get my bag and go, before the bell.

I am losing my mind.

Bells. Ringing now.

She's downstairs. I hear her. Moving from room to room. Living room to kitchen, that's all there is. A utility once. Then the kitchen a kitchenette. Divide the space how you will, there is never any more of it. Confined, then coffined. Speak for yourself.

She moves, I hear her. The rustling of a skirt. How hear that? And yet I do.

Is this the first impossibility?

The kettle, the telly. No, the telly, the kettle. Priorities.

I think she knows. Not going to school today. Not going to school much any more.

And here she comes. Plunge to the side of the bed. Not under. It isn't comic capers.

Hesitates, I hear her. The breathing outside the door. How hear that? How not?

She knows, and has decided.

I have been invalided.

Circling the librarian. Where she goes, I follow. She goes nowhere. Human company, all the same. Not to speak to. See that she sees which books I. Taking nothing in. Robert Owen's utopian vision. History of syndicalism. Sick of all that I.

Something South American. Venezualan, is it?

Leaps out at me.

To us this life appears abhorrent. We long for nothing more than for our death.

Try again.

We abhor this life. And long for death above all.

Below nothing.

Not any more forbidden. When that happens, all goes to pot. That's what they say. Lord of the Flies country. Not that I ever. And to prove them wrong, here I am. Pissing in the staff toilet. Not for the first time. For the second time. Noticeably cleaner than ours. Notably. To be expected. They are not animals. We are animals.

Nobody about. Till suddenly there is.

- Sir, I say.

Sir too taken aback to reply. Don't give him the time to.

Wonder if back in the staff room he will tell. A murmur above the smoking heads. That Prendergast was in our loo. Some such. Loo in lieu of bog.

One more taboo broken, my shrunken head says.

Hats off to Hannigan. Splattered the Head with ripe tomatoes. Overripe, at that. Took his inspiration from Tormato, I know it. Admires Dalí pushing a cousin off a balcony. Some such. Buckets of blood.

Always going to happen. Glad not to be at assembly to witness. Means they can't get it out of me. Still, never got to see the red mess slide off it. The Head's face. Priceless.

Own rebellion less visceral. Consisting entirely of unacted-on thought. Accompanied by piercing look.

Can you see me now?

Her rage at my charcoal drawing of her. Saw it at the parent-teacher meeting. Too lifelike. Too unalive.

Reignites the old hobbyhorse. Yes, she'd burn all my toys.

- You can still do art as a hobby.

My treachery is, am coming round to. Need a clean shirt pocket to put my pen inside. Am a draughtsman, and who wants draughtsmen now?

Without money I will gravitate back to here. To her.

Burn me alive.

Tie off, for good. The purple and black and gold and eagle crest. A bit Third Reich, in truth. In lies. Crest an oystercatcher.

I left an age ago.

I left. That was me leaving.

Mrs Mukerjee, I remember you. You have forgotten me. With the other undesirables.

Life, the old douchebag, makes me up as it goes along.

What do I still have to defy? Whatever's next.

8

The sadness of departure. Her only son.

Mr Mellon kindly. Normally a Sunday driver only. Vintage make, immaculate interior. Easy on the cobbles over the last stretch. Through the fairytale pillars.

My only mother, but the sadness hers.

So serious with my suitcase. She turns her face away.

Nothing dries in this wind.

The salt sea. The fairytale key, handed to me.

– Don't lose it.

Something moving in the stone. A shadow out of the dark. I know her.

– Hello.

– Hello you.

– What were you doing in there?

– Just standing. There used to be a convent here. I like the silence.

– Did you want to be a nun?

– No.

In the light I place her.

- ¿Te gusta la clase de español?

- Sí. ¿Y tu?

- No.

Our footsteps over the cobbles, in the drizzling rain. Out of step at first, then not. I know where we are going.

The dark I always wanted. Again at last.

Thank you, Lord.

Home for Easter. Out of my cave at last. Resurrectionless.

Stagecoach, standing room only. To Dundee at least.

The strap above my head. Unmanly to stagger, OK to sway.

Get it again, a feeling. Not a feeling, a thought. Not a thought, an absence.

No I at all. Only the place where sensations meet. I am what I see. What sees me. So there must be me. Me the meeting-place.

Could do anything at all. For instance, scream. Test the theory, be carted off for it.

The silvery Tay. A seat soon.

My feet are real.

Knocking that never stops. Can't be the maid. The maid would stop. They are called maids, right? Clothes strewn, throw last night's on. Open a crack.

Hannigan.

- What the hell?

Stop-off to see an uncle. Dying, allegedly.

Great big grin at the sight of the place.

- I see you've gone to the dogs without me.

Unwashed shirts hanging from hangers. No room else.

- Must be hard for a wanker like you to get from bed to basin unseen. It's like Rear Window here.

- What time is it?

- Opening time.

Early for stovies, cheese and pickle doorstop sandwich instead, washed down with Export. Breakfast.

- Did you read that Nausea I gave you?

- I did.

- Well?

- It was good, but not the kind of thing that interests me any more. I've given up on finding the one book that explains everything.

- The one book that explains everything is exactly what I'm looking for.

Sitting in a schoolrom chair in the secretary's office. Professor Dorman's room adjoining. Not late for my appointment. The second this term. Attendance record less than exemplary. Nervy after last night's shaving. The whole head, in the kitchen. A North Uist barfly the barber.

He comes in and out.

- Thank you, Mrs Robertson.

In and out more frequently now. Pacing between the two rooms, in effect, hers and his. Sitting uncomfortably, obedient, not catching his eye. Catching hers.

Asks why bald. Lie, say for the part of Mephistopheles in Faust.

He strides in, stops.

- Where is that bastard Prendergast?

Mrs Robertson gestures with her hand.

I am unrecognisable, though not to Mrs Robertson. Mrs Robertsons always can tell.

- Come through.

Who was that black man? Deposited me on the kerb. I on the wrong landing walking into a hall. Into the long bathroom. On my knees at the bowl. Left, I know I did, saying thank you.

Piecing it together. The wallet handed into the station. Almost unbelievable given the locale. Kids throw shit at the windows. And it was all there.

Let in at half six, supposed I'd been out for milk.

- Did I have milk?

- No.

Head aching from more than drink. The bumps either side not matching.

So. I fell down a flight of stairs in the next close.

Wonder is, I'm on the ground floor. Why go up a flight? Where did I think I was living?

You can fall and not feel it, not till later, I've learnt that.

And if there is no later?

Liniment for the pain pungent as the fish. The boss on the conveyor belt with me. Works one day a year like this, the herring season always.

- Overdid it a bit on the Deep Heat, son.

Leaves and the women opposite revert. One picks up a fat one, squeezes.

- This the size of yours?

- Oo, it's oozing.

Belt shuts off again.

- You're tipping them in too fast.

- Youse students are always in a rush.

Wish the boss would come back. Nearly lifting my own weight, in overalls two sizes too big. Plastic cap to round it off.

Salt-N-Pepa's Push It comes on the radio. As if things not bad enough.

And now they're dancing. Making circles before the passing fish.

Rosemary's twenty-first. Or her twentieth. Or her nineteenth.

Miss her as she does the rounds, catch her glances though. I wonder.

This girl's nice to talk to. Flaunts a copy of Poetry London from the Forties. Tambimuttu the editor, she says, as if that means something. Not put off when I tell her business studies.

- Read this, and then read this.

Two versions of the same.

Suddenly not at a party any more. In a perfumed nocturnal garden, holding the Book of Gold.

- I prefer this one.

- No!

Concede worldspace better than cosmic space. Smiles approval.

Speaking spiritually about Rilke. With her long dark hair.

Bombay mix thrust under my nose. Rosemary, smiling disapproval.

Seems like I'm the talk of the town. Stupidly spill all, when will I learn? Said to Breen in the flat I felt inside out. Only lately. How explain? As if my skin flipped. Nothing inside at all, as if have to search the outside for what should be in me. Feeling along a wall for my wounds, that kind of thing. Now meet people asking are my outsides out yet. Two so far. Make a joke of it, all is well. The error of my ways. Supposing we all feel like this at some point. Do we? And not say?

Think, on this hill, I will take up Buddhism. Zoroastrianism. Manicheism. Whatever makes sense of inside-outness. Must be a god for that.

In the meantime, one in the Bobbin to sort me out.

Know this place. Metal piss-wall, cubicles at right-angle.

The Union. Chock-a-block tonight, good excuse to excuse myself from the standers. Shy bladder syndrome, I heard it on the radio. Curse of my. That and these trembling hands. Needed both to raise the pint glass to my lips yesterday. Alarming if continues.

No lock on the door, for ease of rescue presumably. Fine for a piss, as this is.

Hardly in when the door swings to.

– Wait a minute.

Shock as door forced further, into my back as I back into it. Two guys, tall, glimpsed only.

– Remember last night, friend.

No, no I don't, I want to say. No time to.

First punch, harder than imagined. Can't straighten, they are all over me. Seems to stop momently as one takes my head. In untrembling hands. Cradling it, I almost think. Smashes against the cistern, then against the wall. This has to stop. But it doesn't, it won't.

Grasp what's wrong. The silence. Start to make the sounds of pain. Too much pain to feel any, in fact.

Ow! and ow!

It stops. They go.

Blood pissing from my nose, my nose that never bled.

– You all right, mate?

– I got. Beaten up.

A smirk almost. On my own here.

Last night! A couple of Ulster boys, me saying Up the Ra to them.

I'll remember this.

Never did this before. Never broke in.

Put my shoulder into it. Something has to give.

My shoulder.

Almost laugh despite my anger to feel a key. In my pocket all along. Hadn't returned it, will return it now.

Fear that he might be inside after all. Before nothing.

Bastard owes me a deposit, won't see it now. See a twenty on his desk. Dishevelled desk, unmade bed. As chaotic as I. Still, he's the owner, you know. Property is theft and I am thieving. Rightfully mine, if challenged.

Not ever before. Well, since my mother's purse.

Can't very well leave the key now. Places me at the scene, at the time. Starting to think like a thief. Should I leave by the roof?

Don't settle a score pissed. There, that's something to take from this. Else.

Straddles, strangles, and butterflies. The Queen of Lesbia in her Morris Minor. That rusted tin of corned beef in the old dear's shop window. Everything conspiring to irritate today.

A lot of forks and knives in the canteen. Find myself speaking to a girl. Well, her silence unnerved. Not one for chit-chat exactly, but you have to try. The year she is in doesn't tally with the number of years she's been here. Even more nervy, drops her fish. Regret asking. Doesn't hold back, though, once she gets going. Because of her breakdowns, she says. Two, to be precise. How precise were they? Clever people have clever breakdowns. I heard it on the radio.

Her father died.

- Mine too, I say.

That's what fathers do, they die on you.

Have been getting on rather well with the sister of a friend. Not a friend exactly. A sister exactly. She knows people, veers towards them. I know someone, veer towards him. Meet you later.

- Starving, I say.

- You can still get a pizza, he says.

- The only kind left is onion, the barman says.

The thought repels but the mouth says yes. Doesn't take long. Maybe ought to have taken longer. Slips off my plate onto the floor. The godforsaken Dungeon floor.

- Go on, it'll be all right, he says.

Nothing like male reassurance to reassure. Flip it over and tuck in. Find her again. Not interested, clearly. Can't interest her in me again. Try all ways. Maybe ought not to. What happened? They never tell you what happened. Wait, she does. The pizza. She saw.

- Hang 'im. Hang 'im high.

Toryboy squirt, taunting correctness in the Dungeon. Swing-to doors to hell, students' idea of it. Dark basement, cartoon walls. Plastic pint glasses, not for no reason. Hang Mandela on his t-shirt. Otherwise, not a little like Little Lord Fontleroy. Yes, to the waxlike complexion.

Not normally one for. Happy to taunt too, not like this. Afraid of extremities though want to go there. Fear of no meaning once arrived. Out on a limb, the tree trunkless.

Follow from the Union. Not done this before. Bit of detection. Ironside, Maverick.

Gets on a night bus, get on too. Into odd estates. Never find my way back.

Gets off, get off too. Walk behind till the bus goes. Quick now.

No words.

The first punch, then the second punch. Softer than imagined. Unresisting. To the point of enjoyment, perhaps.

Just that flurry enough. The madness drawn out of me.

The hit have to hit, get it out of their system. So we go round the merry-go-round. Man.

I am ashamed of myself.

Skewness and kurtosis. The probability of that girl over there wanting me a steady trough.

Business attracts a certain sort. Not like history of art. Those girls could get you into trouble.

Insist on carrying my books in a portfolio. Insist to myself. Marks me out as eccentric. Till you get to know me.

Know more about art but not the language of it. The language of those girls. Gave one a Rilke poem I copied out. God or goddess of the sleep of cats. She said, Now if I accept this, you have to understand that I can use it in any way I choose. Had a game of darts in the back instead.

Not lacking female company. Civilised to have girls as friends. Of course it's only a matter of time.

Something skewed in me, but I can walk in a straight line. I am walking now, out of the Machar across the high street. Puke, one hand holding onto a railing. It is still morning.

What is the big fear?

Afraid/unafraid of the dragon in its lair. The peakedness of the distribution and the heaviness of its tail.

Might have had a vocation. No, not for a minute. Still. Drop in on the chaplain, see if that life appeals. Thin man, bespectacled. Has he fallen off his bike in the shires?

I am gone, utterly. Unable to utter much, in fact. Slurring, even I hear it. Disgusting him with my pinkie.

– Did you know cats like ear wax?

Brings tea and a side plate, of dark digestives. How many? How long can he bear for me to stay?

I seem to be making him nervous. Thin, nervous man of the cloth. Sees the world reflected in a bubble of Christ's blood.

The cat likes me though.

9

Graduands from all lands. Mother in the rafters. Heart in mouth I'm sure. Choked. Auntie too. These days were made for such. Wouldn't know from their words. As soon as stepped out of car. Boy George on heroin. What did I think of that?

In gown as if born to it. Like Mr Wyatt. May my fingers never be as chalky.

In the next seat even, she. Rosemary. Legs uneven. The seat's. She laughs. Laughter makes it worse, it always does. Serious now.

Hooded she. Rare beauty. Strange, high forehead. Why did I never notice before?

And notice this. Her laughing into me. Hair trembling in no wind.

As always, with sudden revelations, I knew.

I always, always, always knew.

In the magic time. One of two again. How it must have been. In the beginning. Had almost forgot. The happy lunacy.

Take me back.

Pushed a little too hard. Needs her space. Me, I have the universe for space.

Cosmic space, ha. Worldspace.

Not the space around her at all. Her actual body. Its surfaces.

So take me back to Constantinople. No, you can't go back to Constantinople.

Remember I am not on a mission. Exploration a two-way thing. Let the moon plant a flag on me.

She takes me back. Liqueur cordial from the wardrobe.

The war drobe.

Words breaking up today. Loss to blame, even averted.

No body's business but the Turks.

I heard her the first time. Couldn't get out of my. Out of our.

– Not going to work, is it? You living here with her.

– She's my oldest friend, I can't leave her in the lurch.

– I could try to find someone for here.

Smiles, as if at a proposal.

– How soon can you look?

Suicidal dance-hall. Outside it again.

She with booted foot. Kettle-spill, didn't keep it under the tap long enough. Third-degree burns. Or second-degree. Or first-degree, whichever's worst. Numbers all wrong now. Clumping around since. Tonight complete with ball gown. Stunning, I say. And the foot? Hardly notice it. Through my teeth, but you have to. Honesty visits me occasionally.

Leaves again.

With a non-pal to the pub. Couldn't stand not to. Those agri-boys unbearable. Be back for the next dance, I say. Or the one after. Hurt look. Not my finest hour. Safe inside the Machar, the old womb. Regret and drink quick. Long enough to see her Christian ex. In the barlong mirror. Smiling with his eyes. At Judas-me.

And along the long snake of the Spittal. Saying I am heading for the sea, she can't catch me.

Quirks you never saw for yourself. Takes two to see. Like me getting out of bed, always throw the duvet back as if covering someone. She notices, says. I say I don't know why. Immediately I do know. Because it is still in there. My absence. Keep it warm.

- Don't think I don't know what it means when you pick up that book.

- Rilke? What does it mean?

- That girl Sara. From Bath.

Lengthens the a to mock the English. A pastime of hers.

- I'd forgotten all about her.

- Sure you had.

- Are you jealous?

- Of some dark-haired Jewish beauty who tried to pick you up at a party? My party.

- She was never interested in me.

- You think?

- You think she was?

- That's got *you* interested now.

- It was strictly Platonic between us. It was Platonic

between us too, then.

    - Did girls have to throw themselves at Plato too?

    - They wouldn't have got very far with him.

    - She didn't get very far with you, did she?

    - Are you casting aspersions?

    - It's all a bit rum, this poetry.

    - Ha, very funny.

    - Prove I'm wrong.

    - Again?

    - Again.

Glasgow again. Hannigan again.

Heraghty's, Clutha, The Griffin. Necessarily in that order.

And no rush. Years I could be here. We. Get used to we now.

Get on like a house on fire, the two of them. Odd expression, look it up.

It's true, from the very first. Almost jealous. Teresa would kill him, after killing her. Comfort in that.

- You have horrible teeth.

The prick in the deerstalker actually says this. Might have to punch him in the face. End career prematurely.

Last time I engage him at the ref.

Conscious of the bits of bread between my teeth now. Dissolve with soup, perhaps.

- Yes. Yes I do.

Nonchalant but oddly it hurts. Painful reminder. Of when it mattered. To me. To be the bad-toothed one. In or out of school. I'd never get a girlfriend, Auntie said. I already had. Too much Strathaven toffee. And believed that, till the dentist said congenital. Not genetic? No. Smoked when I was in her womb. Thank you very much, you idiot. The fox to the crow.

My headstone teeth, stalker boy. Will. Rip. You. To. Pieces.

I am the master now, as I have been longing to say. Weirdly empty when you think, when I think, of last time. She is there as spectator. In the gallery somewhere. Don't think to pick her out. Want it over with, as I did not then. Have a curry after. Koh-i-Noor. Not in my gown this time. She of course not in hers. Could have come in her uniform. Rub it in that she shunned it. Graduate entry. More principled, that's not a surprise. Starting to think she regrets it now. Could never say. Nether she nor I. We have to live with. Decisions made in time. Which exists, apparently. Forward and back. Didn't need a degree to tell me. Another one. Lecturing too, it's surprising I took to it. Don't know till you. Some do and some do not. Doesn't faze me. And for all that. Five years, in and out of the mousehole. Gathering the cheese of knowledge, a nibble here a nibble there. Watching out for the traps. I am sorry to say I am none the wiser.

Make the stem flow into the bullets more smoothly. Only thing can think of. An A student, so why's she like this? Blouse much too tight, leaning in conspiratorially. Does one say blouse now? Embarrassing, actually. What am I supposed to do? Put Rosemary's photo face down on my desk? Say I am flattered? Avoid a scene, anyhow. Leave the door ajar next time. What is for next time? Equity markets in Japan. Dilate on Mothers.

Something comforting about cats' eyes, she says. Guiding us in the night. Along the A74, killer road, back from Kendal. Car juddering over 70. Smell the oil with the window down a crack. Needing fixed. Tape buggered too, we can hear ourselves think.

    – What are you thinking?

    – I'm thinking about Percy Shaw, the man who invented cat's eyes.

    – How do you know stuff like that?

    – I teach. You'd be surprised what comes up.

    – Keep your hands on the wheel, teacher.

Something, a badger probably. Swerve after the event, almost off the carriageway.

    – Jesus, what the hell was that?

    – A badger.

    – That was never a badger.

There were three berries on the berry tree. I picked three and my body tapered in the undermost branches.

    Actual tears on the pillow, as never before.

    – What were you dreaming about?

    – An old school friend who left me and went to Shetland.

    – That's sad.

    – We were only eleven.

    – Doesn't make it any less sad.

    – I suppose not.

    – What was his name?

    – Martin.

    – I don't think I ever had a friend called Rosemary. No,

I didn't.

   - Rosemary Fern?

   - She was Rose Marie. Did you ever see this Martin again?

   - Once. He came back to school at assembly time, and got shouted at for not wearing a uniform. He just smiled and said nothing.

   - Sounds like a character.

   - A brilliant guy.

   - I've only ever heard you speak about Hannigan.

   - I met Hannigan in secondary.

   - You're a bit of a one-pal man, aren't you?

   - My dad was the same.

   - Who was his pal?

   - The Man in Black. I called him that.

   - Why?

   - He wore a black shirt. Nobody else did.

   - You should go back to sleep.

   - I don't want to have that dream again.

   - You never have the same dream twice.

   - I do.

Michael Stone in Milltown, with the volume down. Headstones a fortunate defence. Comic capers in a cloth hat that comes off. But the targets running towards. Mad retreat. Dad's Army explosions.

   Hannigan sipping his pint thoughtfully.

   - What was the last funeral you were at?

Fortune's hostage, hampered at the start. Expected a no again.

- If you married me it would always be like this.

- Then I will, she says.

At breakfast. Half dreaming still. Sleep in eyes still.

Move towards and knock her bowl, not over, rocks. We kiss, night-breath and bran flakes.

- Let's celebrate.

- Tonight.

- You have a shift?

- Yes.

- Oh.

- Pick me up.

- OK. Can I tell anyone?

- Wait a bit.

- Hannigan?

- All right, but don't bring him along.

- As if.

Undresses, not that she's dressed.

Did I say always?

Closing the door of the flat for the last time. Hers, so she turns the key.

The place where happiest, naturally. Like different people here, children elsewhere. And yet. A grown-up place where we play most.

In actual fact nondescript. Curtains green, striped and frayed. That's it.

Hang on, she's left her. No, she has it after all. Before nothing.

10

There is the wind against your face and the wind driving you back. If you are still moving forward, the past is more bracing. But if you are carried back with it, you feel its force less. The present moment alone empty. I have to feel yesterday today, the wind, the past against my face. You do see all this?

I'm getting married in the morning.

- Bad form to eye up another woman at your own wedding, Hannigan warns.

- Do I do that?

- You have a tendency to let your eyes wander downwards.

- When?

- When a woman speaks to you.

- I mean cite an example.

- The time we all went swimming.

- Teresa said this to you?

- Not just Teresa.

- Rosemary?

- The pool attendant.

- You're making this up.
- OK, I'm making up the pool attendant.
- So I make Teresa feel uncomfortable.
- At times, yes.
- Is that why she doesn't like me?
- She likes you all right. Just not you doing that.
- I won't be doing that tomorrow.
- Good.
- Can I do it tonight?
- It's de rigueur.

At school in my underpants. That old dream. Brief relief then remember the day. Happiest of my. May well be. In bed never really wanted to get out. For anything. Hard to admit to and never did. Sleep my one masterpiece. In bed the possibilities are endless. Is that why? Starting to sound like an old hippie. Worst sort, besuited. Might have flown to Hawaii, got wed on a beach. In a gadda da vida, hula-hula, all that. Have it in me. And Rosemary? God, yes.

Then what's stopping us?

What stops us?

Adjusting tie-knot in the porthole-mirror. Windsor, I know no other. As I am wont to say. Mum behind, fussing with the collar, righting what isn't wrong. Brush her off, as nicely as.

- If only your father was alive to see you.
- He wouldn't have got to speak today.
- Just as well. He was an awful poor public speaker.
- How did he do at yours?

Smiles into her hand. Bunched, tissue inside no doubt.

- He did just fine.

- Then that's how I'll do.

Several references to the clock. Hands seem not to move, somehow, now.

- It's not too late to change your mind, son.

- Yes. Yes it is.

Where the hell is this? Hanging from the rafters, where none are. No, in a spooky alcove. Those churches are best for prayer that have least light. This is the best, then.

Not helped by the weather, but we knew that. From long-range forecast to next day's. And, anyway, October. Rosemary's favourite month. Loves the light, she says. She said.

No light except our lives' light. I should say that.

Her veiled face. See the eyes through the mesh, if it is mesh. Don't think of grids.

Who lifts her veil? Decided in favour of the father. Should have put up more resistance. Might have wanted me to.

Can take her hand at least. Trembling, mine or hers, hard to tell now.

Lined up as if for the firing squad. Here it comes now, many-hatted. I hope Rosemary knows some of these people. See one I know, having seen before, a photo secreted in a Clarks shoe-box. Who wears Clarks shoes? Of her ex. Reason for attendance? Gloating, I suppose. Always said revenge underrated. Smirks as he slips out a hand. Seeking some advantage, grasp it firmly. His as firm.

Neck tattoo just visible above the collar. That'll do.

Incipient dementia, my aunt. So Mum says. She's seen it before. In her mother, their mother. Interrupting the speeches. Wonder she kept schtumm through the ceremony. Sad to see now. Powerhouse of a woman before, now the wind could. Hasn't her daughter to keep a lid on it. A bit meagre with the invites. No say. Not much say in anything, all told. Happy to keep my head down. The wedding-parapet, ha.

She'll be singing that daft song in a minute.

His speech more about him than his daughter. Story of deprivation everybody's heard. How many to a bed? No lock on the outside toilet, you had to whistle. Recognition and laughter in the room.

He didn't welcome me into the family.

Absolutely gorgeous. Careful not to say this. Heard said of brides so often in these parts it palls. Hear it now. What to say else? Haven't scripted this. None of this scripted, except by life. My beautiful bride, perhaps. Love grows where my Rosemary goes. Well, not that.

Indecision induces forgetfulness. If it only could!

– You might have complimented me.

– I'm marrying you.

– That isn't a compliment.

– It is, you know.

– Are we not meant to be in there?

– I suppose we are.

– That could be the last dance they're playing.

– Could be.

- You're in a funny mood.

- I suppose I am.

- Budge up. Christ, the stone's cold.

- I can't feel a thing through all this.

- You'll get it stained.

- I won't be wearing it again.

- That's true.

- Are you happy?

- Yes. You?

- Yes.

- Sadly, we don't have any.

Last request, last orders. Lagavulin will do. For her too. We are alike now, sharing a love. Of silence and of safety, like cats. Hotel bars can do that to you. Piano-playing at an end. The till being emptied. Let the room wait a while, it has waited this long. The day's events sifted. Too hard to see. Shifting, again, kaleidoscopically. Don't shake it so. Bright in the mind.

We can't see how it could have gone any better. Hannigan struck the perfect note, I always knew he would. Her dad only unsober by the toasts. Didn't mix much with that lot, either of us. Never saw eye-to-eye with the McNaughtons.

Tawny, to me. To her, golden.

Only the room number gone.

She is holding my hand inside her nightdress. As it holds her breast. A signal to stop or expression of desire for me to linger. There should be no either-or. What the blood says. Listen to it, only it, for once. So doing you see it is desire.

Hers, for you for her. Here we are caught in a paradigm. Of ancient nights. Yet the desire is fresh.

I let it wash over me.

– What are you thinking now?

Steeper haircuts are applied to higher risk assets. What a week away from lecterns will take me from.

Say nothing. Nothing is what I say.

The same as before. The moment when the alchemy's undone. Caught myself in the hotel mirror. Not the one I was looking at. In one reflected in the one I was looking at. Myself in profile. The Adam's apple prominent, the pointed nose. Observer of myself, when I had been inside only. For once inside the action. As in a dream. Undistracted. Who lives like that? Certain creatures, perhaps. Jackal-headed Anubis. Next door's cat. Now it's time to beg at the door again. The milk of human kindness lowered into place. Don't spill any.

Venice like a dream. Of Venice. Sounds of boat horns cut across your soul. How much does one tip the bell-boy? Hate to take out the map on the street. She sees my discomfort, laughs. Ostentatiously unfolds it herself. Today, content for me to hide it away. Today's destination of choice not hers, though she tags along. It's what we do now. We are married now. As we remind ourselves.

– An old church from a horror movie, on your honeymoon? Only you.

– It's not really a horror movie.

– On my honeymoon.

– Wait till you see the interior, the ceiling's by Corona.

- Who's he when he's at home?

- Renaissance painter. Though the building's twelfth century.

- You can take me somewhere nice afterwards.

- I will. Harry's Bar. Hemingway drank there.

- How about a place that has no associations for you? Somewhere new.

- All right. But don't blame me if it's lousy.

- It won't be. I have a veto now.

The wrong platform. No, the right one. No, the wrong one. Trying to read the times, never was good at it, worse in a foreign country. First outburst after a week's perfection. Call it that. Should have been a fortnight. Hardly an outburst. But a harsh word. Can't hear it any more. Mustn't have been harsh, then, or I would. Unharsh word said harshly. In this no-place of a place. No going back to it once it's gone. Perfection. So-called. Not a flaw to add character. A flaw only. In the ointment. Amuse myself with that thought. Amusement a further separation. Me all over. Even the flaw flawed.

11

The house ready. Hannigan's – no, Teresa's – final touches. Waited in myself for the white goods. Even the words revitalising. Springlike freshness, a new start. A house to live in. Have the housewarming on the first. Everything alpha, everything at the beginning. Keep the dream under the bed like a stone.

Concreted over. Could undo that. Have a patch of ground. Connection with the earth, that old falsehood. A hedge to lean over. Split the smooth hedge leaves between the fingers. Crumble up the soil. My father would. Have his own deckchair. Tin mug on a stool beside. Rest a bit. A hardback if the sun shining. Courtesy of Reader's Digest. I am permitted this. Heinrich Schliemann gazing on the face of Agamemnon. Only not.

He is here, in the clear air.

Away under the stair, with the other things there. Keep the Hoover handy. Hanging up a few things. Her coat, my coat. A bag of papers, sort 'em later. Only a moment needed. A few at most. Moments. Yet linger. Rustling this and that at first, then stop. She isn't listening. Subterfuge not required. What is? Only to stand. Because of the dark, perhaps. But the door ajar. Because of the quiet, perhaps. But quieter elsewhere. Just to stand there, comfortably, uncomfortably long. In the near-dark. The almost-quiet. Under the stair.

Can't go back, she says. And don't blame her. Psych psyched her out. Enough madness in me to be going on with. She joked. Don't always see the joke. No man more normal on the outside. I am on the outside now, hurtling. Figure that one, neighbours. The quiet man who, once a quiet boy who. You didn't exactly try to tease me out of myself, did you? Bitterness behind me now. All behind me now, especially what's in front. Don't blame her though. Kept myself out of one in case it made me sane. Too sane. Couldn't have stood that. Couldn't stand what I did do, either. Whatever that was. It is finding me out.

Whistle Test repeat, any old excuse. Rosemary in bed already. Hear her shifting about. Creaky old bed, bad luck not to have got a new one. Assume the marital problems of its previous. Could be that.

Having my single malt. Am a single malt man even at my age. Which is what? Count backwards. Seem not to be able to do that any more. Count forwards, then. Seem not to be able to do that either, any more.

Alan Hull in a Magpies top. The spit of Hannigan, beaked nose and big chin. Singing about a wee wee. Remember the first times, transistor radio. Trying to make out slavered on their smalls.

Single malt, telly, song from another day.

Not lost in it wholly yet. The fog of time.

- I'll know you if I see you again.

Woman at the bus stop. Car in to get fixed, drive shaft

he said. Son in the Forces, her word. My dad, too, in Korea. All had to, in his day. Still have his letters. A few scraps. Precious.

– Get to see the world, she says.

– I've seen it too, I say. Enough of it.

Looks at me oddly then. The bus draws up. I let it go, she gets on. Waiting for the next one.

– Only one stops here, she says.

– Then I'm at the wrong stop, I say.

At me even more oddly. Oddness in her, in me. Couldn't stand to sit with her. Cover your son in the Union flag, for all I care. Let him down, into the earth. Headstone saying he served. Some have to.

She'll know me if she sees me again.

Leaves her too much alone. Hear them whisper it. Among the leaves, ironically. These leaves. Bitten off more than I can chew. Of the leaves. Medicinal, perhaps. Ironically. Could I be cured halfway? Cured of what? Halfway to where? I ask now! Unjust, the whispering. Have to work. Hours not overlong. And not a barfly, don't hit the pub like some. Not often, and with approval. She is showing all the signs. Of one left. What can I do? Foetal position in the morning, stay that way all day, saying I'm with you now? One of us has to. No kind of pressure on her, either way. Not from me. Not that kind of man. It's not enough of a life for her, that's clear. And I? Man enough?

I have green powers. Strange what you overhear. In shops, on the street. Staple of soap opera but it happens. Only, inconsequential. She has green powers, she says. To one in an anorak, woman or man. I am holding a 10-watt bulb, what do I know? And don't want to know. Move away with just those words heard. Carry them to the counter. Good for a minute or two. Ought to have been a poet. Distinguished sort of waster. Want to say wastrel, even. The poet in me. His calling card. I have green powers.

Tears again that mean she can't any more. Won't do it any more. Not only the psych wards. End what she had planned for herself all along. Her whole life long. Had the outfit as a girl. Not feeling it any more. Must she feel it? Yes she must.

Can't become.

Automaton.

Nothing changes. Then small things change. Like the deer with the one antler, rescued from home. Not on the top shelf now. The one beneath. What does that mean? Other than she never liked it. No evidence of dusting. On the contrary. Moved to remove a book? But the top shelf's poetry. Can't have been that. Perhaps she roams the place, picking things up, putting them down again. Not always correctly. Fingering a one-antlered deer. Meaning she misses me. Could have been that. Not that we ask. Once upon a time we did. Curious to know what the other was thinking, now, that kind of thing. Love has its seasons. The spring, the summer gone. So soon.

A tryst, as of old. Not to bring the car, a movie, drinks after and before. Blue Velvet on again. Seen on release with Hannigan. She will like that. Darkness shot through with tenderness. She is like that.

Had to get her out of the house.

No to popcorn. A bad call. Oh well, dive in.

Feel her discomfort, soothe her as one does. In a cinema. Warmer than May her tender thighs.

The man in front has an erection.

- So he does.

After, cuddles along Killermont Street.

Usual mad night bus, good for a laugh.

All going well. Until.

- I hope I never have to see that again.

The air smelling of Hoover. That will be what greets them. Who comes around. Mum seldom. Sometimes a cousin, her side. One has a baby girl now. Have watched Rosemary freeze when playing. Anticipating failure, I've seen this before. Curse of us all, though I have my moments. Thrills her when I do. Not that she would say, but I see. Starting to feel one coming on. Wonder where that comes from. Sudden surge. Have to act when it does, it never lasts. The air stirred, then stale again. Only fouller.

Hasn't packed it away, as she should have. Still hanging where it hung. Her uniform. Uniformly white. Doesn't swish and sway with the rest. Starched, I suppose. As if she could put it on one morning. One fine morning, up with the lark. Something heroic in shift work. Did it myself once, in the fish factory. The herring season, Aberdeen. Up all night. She also. Graveyard shift. Mortuary shift, we called it. For all the grief for her, brought us close. Tales of the ward. Laughter in dying. When the tears dry.

Bliss in that dawn. The whole house of cards. Domino effect, any pub metaphor will do. Not a pub, a staff room. As good as. Even some pipe smoke, imagine. No need, I see it. And the others. Smoking their heads off, literally, imagine that. The blue pure, the mouth's grey, cloudy. No fire without it. No fire in Armenia either. Watching in a corner of the room. So much for openness. Empire at an end. My child will never know it, if we have. Might be another one. Taking over the globe. Can't see it, but you never know. A new idea. Or old idea returning. Happens like that, in waves. The market too. It's what I teach. The market always moves in waves. The market then retraces with black bodies.

Tum-ti-tum.

Haven't stood in a queue in an age. Not one like this. An age ago was the Apollo. Still mourn for it. Never been inside the Hammersmith. Hannigan has. Still has a life, of sorts. London on a whim. Permitted to join him.

Teresa unable to conceive. Or he. Not sure how it's put.

Waiting for the jester to appear. Can't say I've high hopes any more. Age doesn't come alone.

The support contending with the hubbub. A hometown boy. I'm getting riled.

Find myself the first to shout.

- Orchid Girl!

Strums and smiles.

- Maybe later, he says.

Thin clouds offer little support or resistance. Jargon will see me through.

A fortnight of long walks and curries, otherwise she will be induced. She, or he? We know it's a he, we wanted to. Not two for mysteries. A neighbour will take care of her. If I happen not to be there. Traffic on Kingston Bridge.

This job is easier with my mind elsewhere. Nice that elsewhere is on Rosemary. For once, she'd say. If I told her.

Why do I never tell her?

Long conventional gilts.

Otherwise and elsewhere. Story of my.

12

I've done it now. No escape without injury to others. What a thought to have!

Gave us a queer fright all right. Heartbeat lost, I knew it was. Them all descending on us.

I am fully awake as I never was.

One more human for God to try to know Himself.

Impressed with Rosemary beyond words.

Find them.

A fortnight home. Longer than we had for honeymoon.

I am standing at the mantelpiece, looking on.

We don't know what we're doing.

Bath him. I can do that. Every night I do. The white towel with the hood, folded on the sink. More of a swirl about. A hand on the neck always. The touch of the water stops him roaring. Mollified sobs. I hand myself the towel, or seem to do. Mustn't interfere with time. Onlooker only. Not a bather here. And then I am, lifting him out of it. Clutch to my chest, the wet seeping through to my shirt. A blue shirt today. Dandle on my knee, the heater on. Tears about to start. Quick, sing. Vary the fish but always end on mackerel. When the boat comes in.

Helping him unwrap. Doing it all, in fact. The Christmas tree leaning to Mecca. Rosemary with the camcorder. Didn't go overboard, as I thought she would. Says you don't need to at that age. At other ages she will. Plastic train like Casey Jones's. That one mine. Immediately put aside. He will grow into it. As they say they do, inspects the box. Rosemary not handing over, won't consent to be filmed. Her hair. Her dressing gown. See the stains on the collar, where she burps him. Onto the next thing.

Start the cooking soon. Chef can drink.

A cot beside. Look again! A Moses basket. So tiny so soon. Reverse of how it was, it always is. No room to rock. Wedged. Hardly in it. Asleep on her nipple, I never managed that. Not that I'm. Never understood how some men could envy theirs. Happy for him to be here. The bed, the heart, full.

Charlotte Rampling in distress. In Stardust Memories. Not quite. Getting panicky alone. Not that she's ever alone now. Has Roger. Has me in the evenings. What's left of me in the evenings. Must get back to work after, she says. Can't say she never liked it. Do I? Never stopped to ask. The air rushing, can't stop now.

Can sugar give you worms? The sort of thing you never look up. Can't very well insist it doesn't. Can't insist on anything. Have to be watchful. Tears don't help. Maybe too isolated here. Not that we're far from. Her mum gone, mine no help. Have to take Roger to her. Still can't abide. A nanny out of the question. Really? Mistake to ask. Not my first of the day. Not my last either. Retreat to the study, that isn't any more. Casually the book on wildflowers. Open at milkwort.

- You can't play Lead Belly to him.
    - Why not?
    - He doesn't like it.
    - He does. Look at him.
    - He dances like that to test card music.
    - They still have the test card?
    - Put it off.
    - What does he like, then?
    - There's a tape in the car.
    - I'm not going out to the car. Lead Belly's fine. I'll put on Black Betty.
    - Put it off!
    - All right.
    - Sorry. I don't want him growing up, listening.
    - What's the matter?
    - That man was a convict. A murderer.

Buy me a blue suit, exchange it for a wreath. Odd what persists. This from a glance at a book in a bookshop. Not the book bought. The book bought hasn't persisted. I am at the counter, turning the book over in my hands, but it is blank. Pay the cashier whose face, too, is blank. Indeterminate gender. The shop I know. Walking its airy aisles. Airy but narrow, how so? A self-help book for Rosemary. Conquering Panic! That's the one. Accidentally at the poetry shelf, eye one spine. The Temple Monster. Elide the two. Conquering Panic with The Temple Monster. Have to pick it up after that. Compares unfavourably with A Toccata of Galuppi's. My schooldays Browning never left me. Nothing to see here. Vacant vignette. How know that accelerating through air I will recall it? Moment by moment. Buy me a blue suit. Exchange it for a wreath.

At a fencepost. A country stile, isn't it? So many miles to somewhere, so few to somewhere else. She standing in the long brown coat, buttons like eyes, like the eyes where? The royal tombs of Ur. Standing proud. He on the little ledge, serious, soldierly. Well wrapped up. I approaching. In a moment it will be gone. In a moment it will be another moment, with the feeling gone. It is going already. Will I remember it? One moment to steal from this godforsaken. Rare perfection where nothing perfected. Say an exact constellation. Rightness revealed. His cream-coloured crew-neck peeping out of his brown jacket. She with hair tied back. To think it could be like this at other times too. And won't be. Why? I approaching. I, I, I.

I'm to blame for having given him Smarties, it seems. Don't even resemble Dispirin. No matter, never mind. Argue it out later, as we will. Gastric lavage not an option. Activated charcoal less risky. Keeps the drug in the stomach lining till it's expelled, some such. Hardly listening. Watching. His laboured breaths. Mine keeping time, almost. Rosemary weeping.

How a two-year-old could. Not sufficiently out of reach, it happens. Never mind that she was the last to. Argue it out later.

Happening more and more. Medicine cabinets a thing of the past.

The black liquid into the funnel. Hold him down.

Watch where he retches.

Of course intent inconceivable, but they have to ask. Mistakenly think, his intent. Suicidal two-year-old? No, us. Murderous us.

In the hospital where we beamed before, avoiding, not avoiding, accusatory glances.

We failed.

No, that's right. Nothing to do with their rubbery feet. Electricity operates in a circuit. Words to that effect. If I was flying a kite, I'd be offering a route to earth. Be charred. Not so a bird. Unless touching two wires at once, and a difference between. She is not seeing it. Roger didn't even ask. Rehearsing our answers for the questions he will ask. Rehearsals not going well. Why can't she see?

See him in the mirror stabbing an eye.

Backwards, amazing, a little girl's glue ear in the paper, I can read that.

Indigo is in. Can't bring myself to call it a smile. Frown, even. Hate anthropomorphism. Pathetic fallacy, even. The man who taught me that a right bastard. We weren't discussing rainbows. And here I am with crayons. Life took a turn, didn't it? I am too careful with the colours. Respect a child's faculties, who said that? Any old colour will do, until you think so, but no. Specifically the wrong one needed. She passes with the nappy held away. Considerate. Time to ditch 'em. Good he can even handle crayons. Perfect pincer movement, look at that. Violet her favourite. Now she's said it, mine too.

The snowball grows. Me panting in the white. Bent over, panting, for fun, not wholly for fun. Rosemary laughing.

Roger serious, all children are. Take it too far. Carpark stones roll into it. Pick them off. Save some for the buttons, she says. The eyes.

For his sake, of course, and then for ours. Not done since childhood. Or maybe as students we. No, not allowed, it seems. Remembering that time not allowed.

The kitchen for a carrot.

- That the best you could do?

- Didn't want to waste a good one.

- Waste?

She's right, of course. Show it with a blush. The cold to take the blame.

We remember laughter.

- Was I dead or alive?

- What?

- Was I dead or alive?

- You weren't dead or alive. You were nothing.

- Nothing?

- Nothing yet. It's hard to explain.

- Were you nothing too?

- I was alive.

- He means before you were born.

- Oh, right. Yes, I was nothing too. We were all nothing.

- Am I alive now?

- Certainly.

- Is Mummy alive now?

- Yes.

- Are you alive now? Are you alive now?

- Yes.

- Daddy has to go to work.

The barber knows. He sees the flush spread. Head down, I look up. Devilish perspective. Under the sandblasted lettering. A scissor cut, not young enough for the other, though some do. Some do and some do not. Unless an opening appears, I not. Light in the crack. Then boar my way through. Never the hard rock you imagine. Scissile.

Almost seasick with such thoughts. Tumble through the head. One minute calm, the next in turmoil. Careful not to show. Change always disrupts, always in this way. Limit it in life, but needs must. And succeed, largely, but not feeling too large in this chair. In spite of gown. Or is it because? The barber knows.

13

Brief fields of green. One more stop.

Tenements like sea-devils, porthole windows in the stairwells.

Three storeys, count the flights.

Can't believe I knock.

- My aunt lived here, may I come in?

Shut in my face, as expected. It's what I would do.

Breathless as I wasn't then. Or only if I'd run hell for leather. Out the back. On the green.

Wet, disinfected stone. Ajax.

I have a wife and son, and a baby on the way. Dear Aunt, I am alive.

Lovebirds, if memory serves. It does.

Who got your Bible? Your Deutsche Grammophon LPs? Christ Almighty, your Luger?

Doillies under the iced bun stands. A pity you're not here to enjoy this, they say.

At least they didn't play Colours of Day. An awful dirge. That's what you said.

Go to the park. I'm with you there.

Separate from myself watching me separate from myself. At the lectern, naturally. Confidence intervals and hypothesis testing. Yawned stale morning breath, like dogbreath, filling the theatre. They are taking notes. I am separating from myself and they are taking notes. Thorough, I hope.

I don't. I haven't.

Risk and uncertainty. Drill it into their brainpans.

I have to get out of this place.

One looks up with the shyness of the inexperienced. The curiosity. And looks away. Incurious again. Not spotting me on the wall opposite.

Meanwhile there are human factors that intervene. Cognitive and cultural bias.

Do I have to draw them a diagram?

I look down at my notes. At myself in the pot, unstirred.

I curdle.

- If you don't play with me I'll cry, he says.

Then I'll be in big trouble. Rosemary scowl and take him in her arms. There, there. I know, I know. Hide behind the Herald instead. In truth, enjoy it when I do. Play with him. Wall of inertia I must scale beforehand, too much at times. Like now. Try to see the front and back pages. Illegible. As well be Chinese. Forgotten how to read, it seems. Better to slay the giants in the castle. He wide-eyed, really believing. Is this normal? I wouldn't know. Only son of an only son. Another on the way, God willing. Christ, I am turning into my mother.

Oh my child.

It's a new thing, but it will be a big thing. Get in at the beginning. Pay dividends, literally. He nods his head, I can't read what the nodding means. And then I can. Interest but not approval, as yet. The days of chalk and gown already gone. Not everywhere, he says. Once it's gone, it's gone, you know how it goes, I say. Words to that effect, I can't hear them now. Turn up the volume.

- Think about it.

- I already am. Thinking about it.

Has to add that to make the tense consistent. Academic to his fingertips. Dusty with chalk, but the brain still works. Ideal foil.

- Well that's good enough for now.

- Instead of.

- How will that work?

- It'll work.

- Just like that? With a baby on the way? You're not touching our savings.

- I won't have to.

- Look, if you've thought it through, I won't stand in your way.

- I know that, I appreciate it.

- Appreciate me, not it.

- I thought this would take all night.

- I can see how unhappy you've been. I want us to be happy.

- Thanks.

- That means me too. Don't forget.

Movement in the sound booth. I look up. A couple hard at it, by the looks of it. Standing room only. Laughter rippling along the rows. Muffled now. Covering themselves up, I expect. I carry on, the old pro I am. A bit stirred, truth be told. Tell it.

Cat on a hot tin roof. You either have or do not have a flair for it. Gift of phrase, I tell him. The kraken wakes another.

- Business is our line of business, Cairns says. You're too flowery.

- Well, flowers are flowery. And really are real.

- I say we hire somebody.

- Not yet.

- We'll regret it.

- I never regret.

He laughs.

- Regret is all you do, he says.

Must have been a pained expression, I see him back off. Let him know who's boss. Who will be boss.

Cold wax over the bottle's lip. I must be somewhere. Get deeper in. Oil painting, a gable end, a roof. The table a simple affair. Who joins me? Nobody yet. Must be waiting, then. Or not waiting, a solitary drinker. Can be that at times. Hard times. Or just perplexed. Life at a crossroads like an old blues man. Self-regard in this. My life not an old blues song. Is one playing now? A speaker above my head. Crackling to life, who said that? No, not the blues. Nothing that chimes with how I feel. Not much ever did. Have to invent a new music. A new line of business, more's the pity. Make amends for that with this. The contents of a glass. Hard stuff, I expect. Think I'll make it. Anew.

- Might a velvet divorce be on the cards?

Rita at the kettle, hands on hips. Effort to be steamy herself. Make her words purr. Nothing in it. Flirtation for purposes of ego I go along with. She has used the d-word before, if memory serves. It does.

- How do you mean?

- Oh I think you know what I mean. So when did you decide to go solo?

- Not solo. Cairns is joining me.

- Ah.

- You know Cairns?

- Of course!

- He'll be the brains of the outfit.

- And you'll be the.

- I'll be the bigger brains.

- I like the sound of that. Well, good luck.

- We'll only be across on the south side, you can drop in on us.

- People say they will, but they don't.

- That's true.

- Sayonara soon, then.

- By the way, only the Czechs call it that.

- It's a Japanese word, no?

- No, Velvet Divorce. The Slovaks call it Gentle.

- I was like that. She was like that. I was like, Like what? She was like, Not that. I was like, Like this? She was like, No, this. I was like, Oh that. She was like, Not just that. I was like, And this? She was like, No, not that. I was like, Then what? She was like, Less of that. I was like, Is this it? She was like, That's that.

Well, this is something I'll miss.

When an old Keynesian leaves the crease. Good one, Pettit.
He likes it himself. Smiles into his mug's meniscus.

Committed to the flames. That's one hell of a way to end a
standoff. Sometimes see myself in such. Commune or sect.
If I could throw all away. The women ravishingly holy. They
bring you things, they can't help it. They are resolved to
be demure. It would be so easy to be a saint. You think it
wouldn't, but it would. If this was just about spitting out the
dummy, I could do it. Better to take the low road, where
all the sinners go. Business no good, the bearded weirdo
said. Not like this one. Randy Newman gone wrong. Mister
Retardo. Waco wacko.

You want to do it before your gut protrudes. No one
believes a pioneer with a pot belly. Imagine Christ with
one. Disappears on the cross, I expect. Was sanding the floor
when I caught sight of it. Just the way I was doubled over.
Still. Got to watch that. Rosemary quick to recover, learn
from her. Not that I have breastmilk to help. Is this vanity?
Rosemary says it's vanity. Doesn't stop me, though. Might
appeal to her vanity too. Won't want me waddling beside
her. If we ever do go out again. Almost said step out. Christ,
I'm turning into my dad.

The strip lights, the humming air conditioning. Half-alive
in a place like this. Half-dead. A jumped-up technical
college, Hannigan says. He would. Give it its due, better
than before. Could hardly be worse. Can't say any of this in
my valedictory.

And that is that. Weak ending but it seems to work. See
one wipe a tear away. Could be wiping a tear away. Might

have had the hots for me, it happens. But you don't touch the goods. Or you could. Frowned on, though. Not like in school but all the same. Not exactly honourable. This, dare I say it, is my honourable phase. Embarkation induces such. And I am embarking. Cairns my companion. What have we got to lose apart from everything?

Couldn't do it any more. Be that any more. For others or myself. Or for Rosemary. To find myself finally. What? Incapable of surprise. When the chalkdust settled. This the final straw. Unsurprisingly.

14

Hometown boy. Singing to a girl called Hope. I always knew you'd take me back.

– You hate me, don't you?

    – What are you talking about?

    – I don't blame you, look at me.

    – You're beautiful. You're pregnant.

    – This time I let myself go.

    – Don't be daft.

    – I'm not doing this again.

    – That's absolutely fine.

    – You always said you wanted four.

    – Two of them and two of us.

    – That's right, make a joke of it.

    – I'm trying to lighten the mood.

    – Well, you didn't succeed.

    – Plainly.

Contrary to opinion, I am that. And have been that. A meat-eater. Even in my salad days. Even when I didn't know where to put my hands, when they were on my knees. My mouth was itching to rip into the heaving side. All right, I couldn't fell the beast, but I could feast on it. Have you noticed how I like my steaks rare? It's no coincidence. I'm a meat-eater. I have it in me to be a meat-eater. Contrary to your opinion.

- Why not go to your mother?

    - She hasn't got that kind of money.

    - As if!

    - You think she's minted? Look at where she lives.

    - That's why she is minted. She's got no outgoings.

    - Well I'm not going to her.

    - Which leaves Old Bill.

    - And?

    - You really want to hook up with him?

    - He's all right, Old Bill.

    - No he's not.

This is the tree I looked at all my life. Even when I wasn't here. Especially when I wasn't here.

It's trunk and its lower branches from the living room. Its trunk and its upper branches from my bedroom.

I looked through the branches in the winter. Never managed to look through them in the summer.

It's the winter tree I like best.

Now I'm in its branches.

- Banks? Don't talk to me about banks. It should be obligatory to rob them.

Laughing in the Cowboy Accountant's. Nervous laughter. Not certain we can see the month through.

– What you take out now you put back in again later. Remember that.

Once did the books for Lena Zavaroni. Well, not Lena exactly, the company. The one on Rothesay, Zavaroni Ices. More flakes in the shopfront's paint than in the shop. All the same, tragic what happened to the mother.

– I used to go there as a boy.

– We all did, son. And now look at us.

– Sit down and talk me through it.

– You've read the business plan. It's all there.

– And now I want you to talk me through it.

– I won't beg, you know.

– All right, I'll do it.

– You're kidding me.

– You want me to withdraw my offer?

– I'll never understand you as long as I live.

– Fine. I don't want to be understood.

– Why is that, do you think?

– So you do want me to withdraw.

– I'd like you to be nicer to Jean.

– Look, this is your business. And that is my business.

– No interference ?

– No interference either way.

– Just be nicer, that's all.

– I don't do nice.

– Don't miss the birth.

- I won't miss the birth.

Down the lift and into the world. The lift works now. Only pop my head in to say hello. To say goodbye. Sole occupant of her floor. Health and fitness outlet. Need to speak to somebody. Say I should have used the stairs. She shrugs. Machines all over the shop. Wife in labour, I say. Better get going.

Feels blasphemous putting on the radio. Blaspheme life. Sir Henry Wellcome and his Museum of Man. Unbelievable. Wellcome to the world. Don't jinx it.

The traffic murder but I'm there in time. In a disabled space. On the maternity suite radio Hallelujah. Unbelievable. Time enough to repark the car. She doesn't think so. Her worried look the last I see.

I miss the birth.

It's about how many things can be borne in mind. So Hannigan says. You're in a queue in some minging chippy, but other things are going on in your life. In your head. So you're all right. But the hungover guy behind you, the depressed wee lassie behind him – for them, there's only the present moment. And it's hell.

- Hell is a minging chippy?
- It is if it's all there is.

Wanted out because of the soullessness of the place. To come to this. Fishy smell off a burnt switch the only life.

- We'll clear those whores away for you in no time.
- That's not what I meant.
- It's not?
- Well, yes, it is. I just don't want any trouble. For them.

- You want me to *induce* them to go?

- Christ, no. Don't be threatening anybody.

- I meant offer them money.

- Not that either.

- What do you suggest then?

- Can they not start work a bit later?

- After dark?

- Well, after 6 o'clock at least. Clients are normally gone by then.

- I'll put a word in for you.

- Put a word in? You were talking about clearing them away a minute ago.

- Listen. Once this place fills up they'll be gone. I've seen it before.

- How long will that take?

- Not long. They'll lower the rents if it gets sluggish.

- Oh good.

- Don't be daft. Not for you.

- Why not?

- You're new to this world, aren't you?

- Oh Jean.

Slumps in, cut above the eye. Again.

- Bastard, Cairns says.

- Not his fault, she says. Mine.

Reeks of booze. Not that that.

- Put down the phone, I say.

- That's right, do nothing. Slap Old Bill on the back next time you see him.

- *Hold* her.

Christening number two. A meagre affair, this one. Priest looking over his glasses at me as I do the reading. Acts 16, verse something. Zero absorption other than Lydia, a dealer in purple cloth. Careful. Too good a job and he'll be asking favours. Couldn't stand to be a hypocrite in that context. Back to our place for a bite to eat. Not the priest. Even the vino cheap. Rosemary so far from the plate, up to me to step up. But can I?

- You take no interest, she says.

    - I take an interest.

    - What's the matter? A daughter not as good as a son?

    - You know that's not true.

    - I know it, but do you?

    - I'm here as often as I can be.

    - Even when you're here you're not here.

    - Not that again.

    - Yes, that again.

    - Look, if it's too much.

    - You think I can't cope?

    - You can't cope alone. Nobody can.

    - Why am I alone? Why am I alone, Martin?

    - It's a bad time for me.

    - No, it's a very good time for you. You're having the time of your life.

    - We both wanted this.

    - We both wanted *her*. Or I thought we did. Stupid me.

    - I want you all. More than life itself.

    - Please, spare us the cliche.

    - I mean it.

It's all about the song, they say. You trust the song. But look at the monkeys who wrote some of those songs, in Tin Pan Alley, in the Brill Building. The songs they made Billie sing. We're in love's kindergarten, learning from A to Z. As if she'd be strung out and acting like some wordsmith. I'd rather trust the singer. If you can find one to trust, that is. Who is there to trust now? No, music's abandoned us.

- You don't like the song? I'll turn it off if you don't like it.

Content with your discontent. That's the state of being to aspire to. When you become a father – or a mother – your life is over. In a good way. Not all good. Kids never do see you in your prime. No. In their prams they see you in your prime a moment then it's gone. And they never remember.

I remember.

15

Blackbird on a milestone glimpsed from the car. Turns towards me, instantly, a world of dark.

Is it something out of my own past? Out of what, then?

Experienced only a handful of times, if that. Yet sitting stunned behind the wheel, I feel nothing's more real.

What it would be like to live there always, life permanently pungent in the nostrils. Widen when you think of it. Think too, when I'm dead, there won't be any feeling this.

- There's an awful lot of cooking in an oxtail.

  - Worth it, though.

  - The meat should be falling off the bone.

  - Look at them. They love it.

  - I bet their mother never cooks them oxtail.

  - Don't.

  - It'll be fish fingers and chips.

  - They have a better diet than I had.

  - What was wrong with your diet?

  - Mum. You still cook with *lard*.

  - And?

- It's not healthy.

- They're aye changing their mind about what's healthy. One day it's margarine, the next it's butter. You ate everything I put in front of you.

- Still do. With Rosemary.

- I said to your dad, At least he eats well. That will stand him in good stead.

- What do you mean 'at least'? I never gave you any trouble.

- You were always sickening after something.

- What?

- That was just it. We never knew.

- I'm jumping in the muddle puddles.

Pink wellies, red coat.

Us on a long walk. Long means having to carry her half the way.

- And this is moss. Touch it. It's all right.

- Can I touch this?

- The leaf? Yes.

- Is it fresh?

- Yes, it's green, that means it's fresh.

- Ow!

- Oh, sorry. Those are little thorns. Roses will grow on that bush.

- Prickly.

- There's the small tractor again.

- That's the farmer's.

- That's right. Good girl.

- We don't have any farmers.

- No.

- The farmer's gone away.

- He might be in his house.

- There's the farmer!

Smile at her invention, surveying the land. A hobby farm, it looks like. A bit too neat for the real sort. Tractor almost toy-like.

Smile not faded entirely when I see his face. Hogging the whole window-pane of the hut. Shock to the system, I wonder if that showed. No smile or shocked look returned. Hard to determine what sort. Sneering, perhaps. Leering, even.

- Hullo! Hullo!

Squirms under my hands.

Relax my hold. Must have been a little too tight for her.

Here we are now. The old Citroen, like a faithful mut. Let her down to run to it.

Still hasn't got the baby blues beat. She knows it, I know it. Neither says.

Something about a high-backed chair that's immensely satisfying. Immensely.

Careful how you draw it in.

A three-tiered cake stand in the Willow tearoom. Such a broad smile on her face.

We should do this more often. As we say of all the things we do only once.

Hannigan and Teresa with us too. When *was* the last time? When was the last time?

No kids. They have none. Ours with her father.

Tables cluttered with Christmas shopping at people's feet. Nae class.

Expect, like Hannigan's, my face is the happily-put-upon one. Look around and see them everywhere. Reddened, rubbed by manly hands. Awkward to be here and not the pub.

Inevitably the art school crops up. Hannigan saying it wasn't Mackintosh's masterpiece. Mackintosh's masterpiece was.

- Martin wanted to go to art school.

- Did you? Teresa asks.

- Only, his mum wouldn't let him.

Laughter in which I join. Raise my teacup in Rosemary's direction. Thanks for that, Love, implied.

- Is that a doughnut or a meringue? No, you're right, it's a doughnut.

Realer laughter now. Peel the layers away.

Keep this up and we risk having an epiphany.

Snapping off the branches and putting them on the fire. Norwegian spruce again. I think this was the best tree yet. We say it every year but I think this one was. Save some for kindling. Rat-a-tat-tat, like a machine gun on the flames. Frighten the kids, enjoyably. Needles amassing on the floor. Spruce to pine, sweep 'em up. Too many they dampen down the fire. Still got a bit of juice, smeared on my palms. Breathe in the forest. Need the saw for the rest. Part the coats to find it, hanging from a nail. One touch and I am back, out the back. Dad in his overalls. Would have made a better job of this. Don't think it. A gentle soul, he'd be smiling benignly. Saying, Good work, Son.

Her first swear word. They don't mention that in the books. Not that I ever read any. Pretended to when Roger due, if that's a crime.

Fuck it, at breakfast. Unable to prise the lid off her cup.

Nearly jump out of our skin. Immediate accusing glances. Correctly used in context, I'll give her that. I give her that.

- It's your fault, and you don't even know it.

- Hardly. More likely your dad's.

- What? Last Christmas?

- She has a good memory.

- She must do if she remembers you.

- Can you stop playing that card?

- You don't even know you're doing it. Going round the place, saying Fuck it under your breath.

- Oh well done. I think she's got it now.

Snatches her from the high chair. Mouths to me, Fuck you.

- A basket case, Cairns says.

Odour of Old Bill still in the office. Heavy around my chair. Because he sat there.

- Maybe so, but that basket came loaded with goodies. For us.

- Time to cut him loose.

- Do you think I'm not trying to?

- Try harder.

- OK, OK.

- Has he got something over you?

- A debt. Not of gratitude.

- So pay it back, we can afford to.

- There's no chance. He knows a good investment when he sees it, and we're it.

- Tell him to stop coming here. You can do that. That's a managerial decision.

- Trust me on this. You have to play the long game with Bill.

- We can't just wait around for him to *die*.

- Haha.

- Jesus, that *is* your plan.

Who's that a-writin'? John the Revelator.

Never had to do this before. Pull the car over and wipe tears away.

Revelation afforded only in the car, it seems.

Blind Willie Johnson, you caught me off guard.

Is it blindness does it? Why so many blind, then?

As if that not enough, had to live among ashes finally. His house a burnt-out shell.

Live a life like that and then complain. Only, it doesn't work that way. The down not always in proportion to the devastation. Snatch a toy from a child and see.

If we could pray to Man, would pray to such.

Daughter of Zion, Judea's lion.

Heal me.

Turning stones on the beach. Fascinates, of course. Must be an ancient fear, or is it that we feel we belong here? From such to this. And not knowing the names. Bluff easy when they are this age. Sand worms, I say. Was that a doubtful look? Puts whatever can be picked into his pail. Amassing quite an army in there. To be plumped down into a moat that took some building. By me. Might have had a flair for engineering, who knows? Not about me today.

The weather turns, it always does, to slate-grey.

- Back in the car!

Fighter jets appear from nowhere.

- Well that's not going to happen.

Roger's words after we explain the concept of babysitting. We laugh, partly, and partly don't.

- There's Kathy's boy. He's a wee dote, Rosemary says.

- No, not a boy.

- Because of Marianne? But she's two!

A silence that says, *Precisely*.

- I saw a documentary about fractures in babies, she says.

- When was this?

- Last week.

- Where was I?

- At a wild guess, working.

- What's that?

A thump, then quiet, then the wailing starts. Quiet beforehand never good.

Marianne curled foetus-like on the floor. The bed guard down.

- That was weird, we say after.

Seeing it more and more, guys my age, in similar positions, coked out of their skulls. This at parties Rosemary moans I don't take her to. Have done the odd time. She more liable to experiment. More liable full stop.

A certain weird energy that's impressive, but brewing up a storm. She sees it differently. Sees herself in the mirror and bursts into tears at times. I reassure but no joy. Drugs, any drugs, better at that. Take it all away. Honest reassurance too. Still the girl in the hooded gown I fell for. Though oddly not till then.

- I deal with this crap so you won't have to.

Cairns on the warpath again. Offered to up his salary but no go. Wants as little taken out as we can manage, is a shareholder too. Noblesse oblige. Well, the boy's from Milngavie.

Error to have queried, let him appoint away. His call if it fails.

Ambition is a dryness that can't be slaked. I never thought I had it in me. Rosemary says she never thought I had it in me.

I take a photo out of my wallet and look at it. Of me with Mum in the long sharp beach grass in Lytham-St-Anne's. The hat aside, as compliant a child as you could wish for.

That grass really was sharp.

The hat says Maverick.

Getting into the empty too-much now. After the pure too-little. Danger of complacency, it's always the same. Still, only really the second year. Already had to give up writing. No time for that. Cairns doing it for now. Got a young lad in to copyedit. Kicked out of Uni but a glowing report. First in his year, apparently, but couldn't master Old English, he said.

- Cocksucker, Cairns said.

- Pardon?

- That's Anglo-Saxon. See, it's easy.

Had to tell him off for that. Could have us up at a tribunal for less. Got to watch as we expand.

Have promised Cairns a team of writers. He is dubious but says nothing.

Home suddenly, under the lamp.

- What are you reading?

- A list of words of Anglo-Saxon origin.

- You never cease to amaze me.

Jogging, of all things. At least it's not squash. Competing with my shadow instead. Only this time not. Rosemary's young cousin Becky beside me. She was in the house after all. Expected a no, but never count on youth to conform to expectation. Not even dressed for it. Attractive girl, it has to be said. Hair frizzier than Rosemary's, otherwise two peas in a pod. Awkward that. No sex no interest, Hannigan always says, yet I am interested and sex is out. Hence the stilted talk. So stilted, none at first. Mask that with huff and puff. Must think I'm out of shape. As well she does, I suppose. I suppose I am.

- Over that way's Shawlands Academy, where the race riots were.

- Right.

- I was walking Roger in his pram when the white boys belted past. One of them dropped a knife. In that stream there.

- You're kidding.

- I picked it up and put it under the pram. A butcher's knife. I didn't want any kids touching it.

- What did you do with it?

- Forgot all about it. Then Rosemary found it and screamed her head off.

- Why?

- She had to prise it out of Roger's hands.

- No!

- She made me bring it to the police station. Next thing, I got a letter about appearing in court.

- What happened?

- Nothing. I never got called.

- Exciting story, though.

There to wave him off. Little soldier in his new armour. A photo on the front step. Rosemary keeping Marianne, all snot still and with the morning grumps, out of the picture. It would be raining. That's how I remember my first day. Dad in the Morris Minor, with the wipers going sedately. Mum with me in the back. Only she ventured inside with me. Fast-forward twenty-seven years and I'm not even in the car. Or I am in the car, but office-bound. Rosemary well able to deal with the two of them. Still. Might have gone too. He'll remember this day for the rest of his life, but will I? Of what's left of mine.

What's regret when you feel it immediately?

16

Contra Desiderata. I keep threatening to write it.

– You do that, Eeyore, Cairns says.

May slap it up over his poster. Go placidly amid the noise and haste, etc. Think he put it there to impress the temp. No cause to hire one before. Things looking up. Not exactly noisy or hasty yet, though.

And the estate filling up too. New startups, fresh blood, it's all good. That smiling man in number 10's given the whole country a lift. An inverted Cheshire cat, I said. You watch. The smile will disappear and just the rest of him hover there.

So it's balloon time again. Roll out the barrell. Hoopla and all that.

I have no right to be here.

– You're no fun any more.

Harmless when said in fun, she thinks, but cuts to the quick. Because I've no interest in seeing the latest Bond movie. Has a girl who'll babysit.

– What girl?

– Sam's daughter?

- We could babysit *her*.

- Nonsense, she's seventeen now.

- They shake babies, these girls.

- We don't have a baby.

- What's on at the GFT instead?

- You know I hate subtitles.

A bone of contention, that one. Oh well. Bond it is. Tomorrow Never Dies.

It does, it did.

A mercy she didn't say Titanic, at least. There's that to be said for her, she isn't a sap. And I'm not. Fun. Any more.

Running rings round me. Quite, quite literally. And pleasurably. In Pollock Park. So pleasurably I don't bother with the Burrell. See the Chinese urns another day. Roger is grasping at thin air. Thinner the quicker he goes. Because I do follow.

How long since I did this? Not take the boy out just the two of us. Simply run. An age. Age is the word.

This the place where she asked memorably, Is this wilderness enough for you? Saw a white horse that time. Flashed before us.

Now a boy, my boy, moving at speed. Till he stops suddenly. Suddenly he's afraid.

- What's the matter?

- When Good God died, Bad God made Circle Woods.

Scotia with Hannigan then over the road to the Clutha. Daylight drinking, nothing like it. Telling him my hopes and fears. As if. Attempting to empty the mescal bottle to get to the worm. And we nearly make it. So nearly I fall off my stool. Head cracked but just get on with it. Odd application of my mother's mantra but what the hell. Really a sore one. Bar staff not liking us. Though we don't need them to, we need them.

A dark feeling at a certain point. Drink a sure indicator of mental illbeing. In me. Hannigan not noticing while his face blurs. Eyelashes vivid suddenly, in a Clockwork Orange sort of way. Have I had this thought before?

It will be fun explaining today to Rosemary.

In the hope of ever rising again. Discomfort on the too-comfortable sofa. Sinking in that way. And not because Roger is in the room either. Marianne asleep. And not, not certainly, because of the vent scene, Marilyn's lifted skirt. Not even a recent indiscretion to account for it. The title, The Seven Year Itch, is enough. Rosemary too, squirming a little. Depressing to think the malaise might be general. Like dying one of many, I suppose. Perhaps we should be seeing our own Dr Brubaker. On the NHS, imagine. Adultery a terrible thing, all will have to face God in the end. Actually heard that in the consulting room. Not Barrett, to be fair. Like gibbons, we left-footers mate for life. Or for death, whichever comes first.

Goodwill can never be revised upwards.

There is an underlying assumption of infinite granularity. And then, wham bam, I am back on the pole. A beanstalk, perhaps. Some kind of cane in the fields. I hope I am not a party to enslavement. Dreadful business model, all told.

It is slowly shredding my hands. Soon to be bone alone. That would be something. A skeleton ere I land. Grisly, but for others now. Eyes hooded in death.

There, I've said it. Now let me sleep.

This is the end of everything, Toad. Good to be reacquainted. After all these years. How many? Count them. One, two, three at least. Imperishable classic, perish the thought.

And yet it never is the end. Until the day it is. Comforting thought, I suppose it should be. Another is to imagine things incalculably worse. Famine or flood or such. Or born into misery. Not simply growing into it, as I have done.

How say that when I am perched on her bed, reading of Toad's adventures? For my benefit mostly. One day I will count this a happy day. Not that it will ever be remembered.

There I go counting again. She is here, unaccountably happy. And I not what?

Immured. In a dank and noisome dungeon.

I can see the dreamer not the dream. Somehow I know what the dream is, though. Under those jerking eyelids. I meet somebody's daughter and feel an affinity with her. At a wedding, I see that she is named as one of the bride's five daughters. Alongside each is the name of the girl's father with his email address. Three of the girls have the same father, but his email address is different each time: clearly a dodgy businessman. As I approach the building where the reception is being held, I see that there is scurrilous graffiti about this man, and I feel sorry for the girl. Inside she is dancing with the businessman. Their shadows are on the wall above the dreamer. She is the bride now and this is her dance with her dad. Except that every glance and gesture of hers says he is not. And he knows it. Wounded look. Every glance and gesture, projected on the wall, an addition of salt.

Must be Old Bill. But *she*?

Capable of subterfuge but don't relish it. Wonder at times the extent to which she suspects. Have no inkling. Suggesting perhaps she is capable of subterfuge herself. Not that I have much to conceal. Apart from everything. For instance this cat in the window. Feed it scraps before I leave. Not scraps. Bloody great chunks of tuna. Or other item. If she misses them she never says. Might find in fact she approves of the feeding. Might find in fact she is at it herself. Don't think to ask. In case she says not to. Can't leave first thing to the sight of disappointed eyes. Not another pair.

Could the Tarot have predicted it? This my thought as word comes through. Of Gran's death. Over the phone. The telling bone, Catweazle called it.

Only last night Gillian did the reading. Strange girl. There to babysit, ended up babysitting us. As we sat aghast, staring into the future. The Empress and Death.

- Give me that, I say.

Seem to spend my life moving towards a held-out receiver.

- Are you all right? Stay there. We'll be over now.

No, doesn't want Rosemary. I can hardly tell her. Say I will scout things out for now. Arrangements to make. She knows.

And I'm in the car suddenly. Put the wipers on in error. As if wanting there to be rain. Wash it all away. Mad wipers.

In the car thinking, a cold kitchen with a chequered floor. Reach for the radio.

Last night I drove Gillian home in the rain. Doubtful of her credentials. Don't want mystery in someone minding the children.

Automatic I should have flicked on the wipers, then. One moment knitted to the last. So it goes.

Till a stitch is dropped. No mystery in anything.

Turn it up.

- This is not a gloomy cave.

Sweet girl, she says it like she means it.

I have her in my arms. I do not have her in my arms.

Meaning I am so absorbed I can't touch reality. It can't touch me. Is that the point? So I look intently. And more intently. And more intently than that. Peeling away the layers of self. Extraordinary how many. Try it. Till a serious-looking three-year-old is in my arms opining, This is not a gloomy cave.

Up to the birthday-cake building on the hill. Faces of those emerging from their cars eager or strained. Sit on a child's seat outside the room, the corridor a washed-out green. Rosemary by my side, comically. All of us like that, we are all laughing. Grown-ups on tiny chairs. Have to be hushed. Be good children.

Roger's teacher beckons. Older than I'd pictured her. That's as well, I think. Shows us his jotters. Handwriting could be neater, I suppose.

- Is that an Irish accent I detect?

- Tipperary, she says.

- Lovely.

How does she find him in himself?

- Not a bother, she says. No, wait. Once he flushed a girl's bobble down the loo. Inexplicable, really.

- He's tormented by his wee sister, Rosemary explains.

- He has a remarkably vivid imagination, she says.

For instance, told the class I'd been abducted by aliens.

Spirited away in a flying saucer. Only to come back again a different man. A robot this time. Laughing say I was the same. A vase of flowers set in front of me, I made a head with roots and a knife entering the nape.

Time's up. Squints at me suspiciously as I scrape back the chair.

Goodbye, Piccadilly! Farewell, Leicester Square!

Can contango and backwardation exist at the same time? You bet your life. In truth, only dipped into the file, looking over Cairns's shoulder. Miss writing the stuff but no going back. Not even Cairns does it now, only spot checks. This one spotless. The new bastard the real thing. Looks at me as if he can read my thoughts. Only thing is how slowly he types. Different in the old days. My auntie in Berlin did better. I can hear her now, in the other room. Not *now*. You'll keep the boy awake, Uncle said. I like to be kept awake. Sleep has too many demons. I know this means I do. Ward them off by whatever means. Jargon as good as any.

A function, held in the function room, in honour of a functionary. My good wife by my side. Doesn't normally make these dos any more, so sprang a surprise. As if to catch me out. Check if anything sounding so boring could exist in fact. And does. And she immediately regrets. Not that she makes a display but I can read the signs. I ought to be able to by now. Legs crossed and left foot nodding sagely. In sympathy with the metronome of dullness swinging through the universe. Bringing my eye to the tip of her red shoe. Matching matchlessly her red handbag. Red such a difficult colour.

Cocktails finally.

- A bit late to be the cocktail hour, is it not?

The waiter grins. Rosemary grins. I am being grinned at. At times like this one could happily kill oneself.

As I am now. Feel it slipping again. This I. Rescue by Rosemary fading. A supporting column, very classical. Time ruinous. That's all right, I can lean on the remains. I will stand in a wind and lean. Emphatically.

Now I am the age Christ was finally. Millstone of a milestone. The miracle would be if something happened. Dear God, let it.

17

And after all, before nothing, The Green Tree. Only stopping for a quick one on the way to Waverley. Working at the weekend. Call it that. In truth, no end to either the work or the week.

This time another time. Client taken ill. Browsed the Grassmarket, then the Lawnmarket. The Cowgate now. Searing heat. Even the down-and-outs have their summer attire.

Despond of Grandstand on the telly. Same old Saturdays. Take my pint, and myself, into the beer garden.

The smokers out in force. A white-tunicked crowd at one table puffing away. Smile at a smile. Which joins me.

Under blue eyes. Red hair.

A little bit intoxicated, truth be told. Reassures she doesn't ever do this kind of thing. What kind of thing are we doing?

- Oh, you know.

Find after a while we have this in common. Can both draw, both wish we had taken it further. She is starting a night class, she says. Away over in Glasgow, in the art school. Always wanted to go there. Both did. Quiet while we think about that.

Reaching for a word, say even the down-and-outs are dressed for summer. She laughs. A very pretty laugh. Say again. A laugh that stirs the very depths of my being.

Throughout, we clutch our drinks. Our free hands find each other.

The hallowed entrance. Fourteen steps like the stairs at home. The old abode. And another at the doors.

This could have been me sixteen years ago. Fresh-faced and struggling with my portfolio. Mathematics switched to business studies was the way to go. The way I went. Till now.

A night class is not enough.

It isn't only that. This Ruth. Sounds like a dream girl, Hannigan said. And maybe I did only dream her. Dreams are real, aren't dreamy.

She is not here as I mill about, select my spot. Even the model is here by now, dressing gown still tied, less obese than I'd supposed. Like my first day at school with a pristine pencil in my pristine pencil case. Derwent Graphic this one.

Now she walks in and nods to me and takes her place. Two people between. And glances across and smiles faintly.

One difference, no rubber in with my pencil this time. Nothing need be erased.

- You are drawing not only space but time. You think this moment can be frozen in time, just because I keep absolutely still? No! If you get your impression of me right then time will be there too. Time is only mortality. I am going to die. But I'm alive. If you depict me then make me alive and dead in the same instant. Not me, obviously. Have you got that? Then begin.

I must say, I thought it would be less intense than this.

Drinks after class. Enough others for it not to seem a date while being one. I suggest the Griffin but am overruled. She smiles that I take it well. In truth, indifferent. As long as I get to sit close, and I do. Lightly brushing arms, legs. Not exactly The Green Tree again, but enough. For now. Art dilettantes, except she. Has a real gift, we all say so. See her blush for the first time. Confined to her cheeks, making her oddly doll-like.

Has a train to catch. I have to leave too. See the know-all glance of one. Let them talk. Queen Street but I think of Central, its glass roof. Under it I carried my little case as a boy. Off to Rothesay in the morning. Same excitement, except I'm not leaving. She is leaving. We press flesh almost business-like as she embarks.

It's not enough. I get on too, a ticketless hero, before the doors close. She goes pale. Kisses me to make me leave, at Bishopbriggs.

What do I do now?

A bit too aesthetic for my liking. No, I like it. And after all, we're only passing through. It's not as if we live in galleries.

She smiles at the attentive attendants, discomfits them. I pass them by like an apparition of air.

I have time for this. Am not in business to scoff. My five-year-old, when each was five years old, never did better.

When we stop for long it means something. Not only to read. Look first, I say. She keeps forgetting, says she will try to be better. It's me dragging my heels as we move from the Bacon. Study for a portrait. Of his friend (I read), Anthony Zyke.

- You think he looks like me?

- No. Do you?

- Yes!

- Because he has a suit on?

- Not just that.

- I could do you better.

- Then do.

Doesn't want to eat here, she says. Would banish cafeterias from all such. Seems almost heated on the subject. That's all right with me.

And in the middle, Miró's Maternité. We inspect it like art critics, step back and stare like dumbfounded children.

- Don't worry about breathing in, just concentrate on breathing out. Slowly.

Her face white as a sheet, eyes pleading. Panic such as I've never seen in her before. Have in fact seen none in her before. Making my own pulse race. I mustn't show that.

- I'm going to have to leave. Now.

- Let's leave, then.

I put money next to the uneaten food.

Outside, the bloody city tour bus filled with eyes.

She leans in.

Victoria Street suddenly. Like a set from The Cabinet of Dr Caligari. Even to me.

Only the Meadows begin to soothe. I walk the whole way with the two of them, myself and her.

What was that about? She doesn't know. It doesn't matter.

I hold and hold and hold.

Hovering, as before. When I leaned against the wall-propped board of the twin-tub. Mum just out of view. Same sensation now. Elevation greater, of course. Yes, seeing it all now. From up above. Must be near the bare light bulb. She likes simplicity. And honesty. I could cut the atmosphere with a knife. Not in a bad way. The chasteness of it all! Keep me waiting. And still. Posing a few steps from her. Not seeing her, though. In profile. Staring straight ahead. At what? The doorknob? She is clearly milking this. I must be passing the test. I am still here, right? Can see the drawing now as I could not then. At an angle. I am perfectly still. Good to be released from restlessness. If Cairns only knew! Drumming up business in the capital, aye right. Or Rosemary. Dare to mention. Can picture her turning away. In disgust.

An unveiling of sorts. Only her shirt over the easel and the top edges of the paper. Her obligatory mannish painter's shirt, worn for a charcoal drawing. Won't have it called her smock. Not quite whipping it off, but an unveiling all the same. Of course I had had a peek. But that was a week ago. She had worked well in my absence. Maybe after all she is at her best when I am not there. Not a thought for now. An unveiling, but my eyes are veiled. My heavy lidded eyes. Can't quite believe what they're seeing. Myself, as if for the first time. Not as if. I am seeing myself for the first time. Through her eyes, which are now my eyes. This suited gent she saw as Gogol's madman. Penguin Classics edition, I even have it. Hair, spikily short and sticking up, I must have run my hands through. Head in profile. Visible ear large. Eyes, or rather eye, intense and staring straight ahead. Not into, at. Something not in the room. Or in the world. Nose wide-nostrilled. Bit of a sour expression. Hair starting rather high on the nape. Chin down, so the eye, therefore eyes, level. Not mad, in fact, I can see that now. Reassuring. No future in madness. But as if known the world. As if known the world and found it wanting.

Linseed oil in the nostrils, but the paints have been cleared away. There is nothing on the bed. Her bed that was ostentatiously covered before, in clothes and whatnot. The duvet is smoothed but not completely. Like a rippling surface of water. She sees me seeing it, offers tea. Nothing stronger at this hour. She has her evening shift to think of. I have to be back too, which is the way it is. I say no. That pleases her. Daylight lovers. Only, with the shutters closed. She closes them now. For the first time. Takes the honesty from the sill, steadies it on the carpet. A deep pile. No word spoken. Undresses, first she. Takes my hand. I can play this game, I know the rules. A moment later I forget the rules. Am all at sea. Am all at sea and as if on the verge of

– Oh God, is that her?

   – Yes, keep walking.

   – What are the chances of that happening?

   – That we walk past my mum's house and see her through the window? Pretty high, I imagine.

   – Don't be sarky.

   – Don't turn round.

   – Can we turn at the top and walk back down again? I want to have a better look at the house.

   – No. She might clock us.

   – Just me, then. She doesn't know me.

   – True. But there's something else I want to show you.

   – What?

   – The swing park I played in.

   – Oh I want to see that.

   – It's only got the chutes and the swings now.

   – What did it have before?

- A roundabout and a frying pan.

- A frying pan?

- Killer roundabout, you're too young to remember.

- Lucky for you.

- There were hardly any cars on the street. We played football here.

- Where were the goals?

- Between the tree and the kerb.

- I bet you were good.

- I was all right. Why are you smiling?

- I'm picturing you as a boy.

- There are pictures of me as a boy in that house.

- Which I won't see.

- My mum would be very grateful to any person who took me away from Rosemary.

- Let me meet her, then.

- Would you let me meet yours?

- You wouldn't want to meet my mother, trust me.

- Have you noticed? There are no kids about.

- Maybe they're all in the playground.

- We'd have heard them by now.

- I like seeing couples in playgrounds with no children. You know it's real love. Why have you stopped?

- It was here. It was right here.

- This was the Old Block, and that was the New Block.

Showing her round, as requested. The place of the bell. And the belt.

Graffiti in my old registration class. Not on it, in it.

Must be more liberal now. Or impoverished.

- This was the Science Block.

Periodic table visible through the window. Hard to make out, she says. Not when you have pilot's vision, I say.

- That's you there, pink, in the middle. Ruthenium.

- What's ruthenium like?

- Hard.

- Not like me, then. Where are you?

- Close to you. Mn for Manganese.

- And?

- Useful. Brittle.

The high rise on the horizon. My eyes keep getting drawn to it. When I stop looking down. I can only look down intermittently. Hard to stand beauty like this for long. Only death would feel right after. Only death is beauty's peer. Strands of her red hair intertwined with the strawy grass. Round pale breasts exposed to the cold. A warm autumnal cold. Harvest moon in the blue. Inside. Outside. I will always remember.

Where else but Hope Street? Risky in town, but Hannigan along, so she could just as easily be with him. To the unobservant observer. No small thing, his meeting her, her meeting him. Starting to exist in the world. All things come to a head, Mum said. Yes, Mum, but not yet.

Drinks in the Holiday Inn first. Awful anonymity.

Hannigan warming to her, I can tell. Ruth is, well, smitten. Likes intelligent men. Hannigan, as he will never hear from me, is the smarter of us two. Old-fashionedly courteous. Ruth likes this.

Get to the Theatre Royal with time to spare.

- This building's haunted, you know. By Nora the cleaner. She always dreamt of getting a big break, and when she got it she was laughed off the stage.

- That's awful.

- She killed herself.

- How?

- I don't know. Haggie, do you know?

- What?

- How Nora the cleaner topped herself?

- Nora the ghost?

- Aye.

- Hanged herself, I think.

- Oh God.

- The translation's surprisingly good.

- Who wrote it?

- Somebody Haldane. Hold on.

I catch Ruth's smile. Perhaps I'm meant to. It tells me she is happy now.

- Seán.

At this moment, she is happy, in the next she might not be. It seems to be going this way. Fluctuating.

- I dreamt about you last night.

- All good, I hope, I say lamely.

- You weren't in the dream, but I know it was about you. About us.

- This sounds interesting.

- I was at the doctor's and he was writing out a

prescription. Then he whispered to me to ignore the first things on it and only pay attention to the last.

   – What was it?

   – The word 'quitter'. It's French for 'leave'.

   – Maybe it means don't be one. A quitter.

   – I know what it means.

The wedding of a friend. Her friend.

   – It will be all right.

   – I don't see how.

   – It will be all right because there will only be us there and the two of them.

Exposure not on the order of service. No order of service, in fact. A quickie at the registry. Knew the woman from that day in The Green Tree. Or knew her face. Amiable enough guy, the groom. So he seemed. Till the girls left together before dessert. Excited talk in the ladies. While the hotel restaurant slowly emptied.

   – It's a bit of a slap in the face you're being here.

   – Come again.

   – You're married, right?

   – Yes. I haven't advertised the fact.

   – Your ring does, pal.

   – What's your point?

   – Would you want your witness to be some guy playing away from home?

   – I didn't ask to come.

   – *We* didn't ask you to come.

   – I'll go, if you like.

   – You can stay for your pudding. Then the two of you can go.

- All right. But you're lucky it's your wedding day.
- Meaning what?
- Just that.

18

- Can we be clear what is happening here? You are the one leaving.

    - You left when you didn't leave her.

    - You never asked me to leave her.

    - I shouldn't need to ask.

    - It's complicated.

    - Oh, please. Spare me.

    - You're not a child. It is complicated.

    - Why are you even with me?

    - Because I love you.

    - You love Rosemary.

    - I never said I didn't. But it's a different kind of love.

    - And it's her kind you're choosing.

    - I'm not choosing.

    - You have to choose.

    - I need more time, that's all.

    - Don't you get it? *There is no more time.*

In a fog of my own devising. That's the truth. I could cut through it, if fog can be cut through, if I only tried. She would be willing to wait if she thought me capable. No, I am capable, but I won't. The fog has got too thick, is almost a stew. Can barely wade through it now. An ultimatum might concentrate the mind. So she had thought. But nothing does. I have spread myself too thinly. And when you are spread too thinly, and enveloped by a fog that's too thick, then you are going to get swallowed up in it. It stands to reason. In those circumstances, it stands to reason that passion fails. It falls. Everything does. Gravity is the grave here.

- No more trips to Auld Reekie for me, then.

    - At least we won't be bumping into each other.

    - And that's a good thing?

    - I think so. I think it's best to be definite.

    - You sound it.

    - I am.

    - You didn't say anything about it when I was in your bed last week.

    - Don't be crude.

    - I'm not being crude, it's the truth.

    - If I let my body decide then, no, I'd never leave you.

    - The body never lies. Didn't I say that?

    - Many times, and I believe it.

    - Then what the hell are you doing?

    - Shoosh.

    - Sorry.

    - I don't just live in my body.

    - That's the only place any of us lives.

    - I have a brain too. One that won't let me sleep at night while we carry on doing this.

- This?

- This thing that you know is wrong.

- It feels right to me.

- No it doesn't. Not if you're being honest with yourself.

- All right, I feel bad that I'm a liar and a cheat. But I never knew I would meet you. I never knew I could have this. And now I can't.

- You'll survive. I'm not sure I will.

- I'm more fragile than you think.

- No you're not. I know exactly how fragile you are. I saw it right from the start.

- Please don't do this. Please.

- Martin, don't.

- Please.

- Christ, don't they have a jukebox here?

Our anguish audible, only the low murmur of chatter to contend with it. The nearest but one table the worst. Zero sympathy from that quarter. Unshaven mocking face. His companion too, even the back of his head affronts. Clearly murmurs encouragement to the mocker. Could punch both their lights out. Drinking their piss-pale lager.

- Why do you even care?

- I don't care.

- Then stop looking over.

Telekinesis not an option. Otherwise they'd be speared by the glass. A shard from the sandblasted window. Reverse letters at the best of times, I don't need it done for me now, at the worst. Anagrammatise too. Yet never noticed that her name spells hurt. Heard only the chime with truth before.

What would I put on? Heartbreak Hotel?

- How was your shift?

   - You really want to know?

   - I'm changing the subject.

   - It was tough.

   - How?

   - Somebody died. A really sweet wee man.

   - You get to know the patients well?

   - The ones that are there for a while, yes.

   - Could it be his death is affecting you now?

   - No, that's got nothing to do with it.

   - What did he die of?

   - Old age, I suppose. His heart stopped beating.

   - They say we only have so many heartbeats. The faster the beats, the shorter the life.

   - The dragonfly's must be fast.

   - They live longer than you think.

   - I thought it was just a day. Do insects have a heart?

   - Sometimes more than one.

   - You know a lot of stuff.

   - Think about all the education you'll be missing.

   - I'm glad you can still smile.

   - This isn't a smile.

Dragged through a hedge backwards. So the mirror tells me. Above the bar. Quick glance enough. And she so pale. Like seeing a ghost flit. Of course there's the white of the tunic, but still. What a pair! No wonder we draw glances. That, and the evident trauma of the occasion. Even with the sound turned down. But the sound is not turned down. Still, no raised voices, though she hushes me once or twice. Three times. Can't always hear my own anger. See it reflected, though. In a face of pain, whosesoever. Hers today.

- Thirteen years!

    - Not from now. From when we met.

    - Twelve years! I'll be what? Forty-seven.

    - And I'll be thirty-five. Your age now.

    - I'll be older than my dad ever was.

    - Only by a year.

    - How do you know that?

    - I worked it out.

    - Where will we meet? Not here.

    - The Green Tree.

    - When?

    - The same day we met.

    - The day or date.

    - The date. First of August.

    - 2011. How will we remember that?

    - If you think you'll forget.

    - One eight eleven. Year of the Luddites.

    - What?

    - When the Luddites started smashing up machines.

    - See, you have interests. They'll come back.

    - Not my passion. This is. Look how well it turned out.

    - It turned out fine. We can still talk like this.

    - Not after today.

    - No.

    - Thirteen years is too long.

- Twelve years.

- It's too long.

- I know.

- You don't mean it, anyway. It's a sop.

- I mean it. I always mean everything.

- Well that's true.

The body numb. First the mind, then the body. A Cartesian duality I never subscribed to. Subscription not necessary. A slight stagger as I rise to go. In her wake. As if about to keel over. As if an exhibit sans handler. Only momently. That bastard looking across again. Seen enough? It could happen to you. A slight paralysis, perhaps. Cruciate, something of that order. Left side noticeably cumbersome. Stagger that way. Widdershins. It would happen in Doctors, wouldn't it? Her choice. Must be a medical student about. Would make an interesting case. In the lecture theatre. Or laid out on the slab. Come to this. After a lifetime's beating. Inert ticker. Unwound by one. So deathly pale. Who loves you baby?

Can't help but touch the railing. Needing to be grounded now. To be earthed. Half wanting and the other half not to hold her hand. See what she will miss. Will she miss me? Has said so, hasn't she? The ground may rise to meet me. Blame it on the ale. Just the two, but what an accompaniment. A dagger through the heart. To put it mildly. Confers a raw energy all the same. Maybe whisk her up and shake this nonsense out of her. Instead keep a steady pace as the Meadows materialise. Parkland when the heart's been torn. The upkeep not too bad. Not the wilderness I seek.

- Is that man doing what I think he's doing?

Half a man visible as if emerging from the tree. As if a comic routine. Swift movement, much too swift to be misinterpreted.

– Those boys'll chase him. See, I told you.

Pale after that, but she was already pale. Turns to amusement for a moment. This is when her hand goes limp.

– That will be me soon.

– Oh you'll find someone else to do what I've done for you.

– No I won't.

– You have a wife to.

– Let's leave her out of this.

– It's what I've been trying to do.

– Touché.

At touché, a woman jogger in grey sweat pants passes. In front of our eyes. Our eyes that turn to follow her. And I do think sweat pants, seeing the patch of sweat on the seat of them. She leaves an odorous trail behind her. Barely discernible. But we do discern.

– You see. It didn't take you long.

– For what?

– For you to start looking at other women. Any woman who passes.

– That's not true. Or fair.

– I'm sorry.

– I'm sorry too.

Quietly holding hands. As if there were no more words to say. On a bench in the Meadows on a cold November day. She in her white tunic. White shoes, wetted by grass. I think she will feel different after a good sleep. Stop myself from saying, You will feel different after a good sleep. Have seen this coming, but now that it does, surprises me. Caught an afternoon train to Waverley especially. Should have got off at Haymarket. No plans, other than to be together. Presumptuous, in her eyes. Not letting me in today. Will sit tantalisingly close to her room, I feel it at my back. The dark glass. No watcher in the shade, except my old self of days ago. The time I let myself out. Stood at the window and surveyed the scene. In which I now sit, quietly holding her hand. But not close. Have to stretch to reach. Her hand limp by her side, meekly accepting mine. Or defiantly lifeless. White tunic, red hair, green grass. Hard not to notice colour. Or the geometry of the park. Go over this again in my mind. It will be emblazoned on it.

On a bench in the Meadows. Within sight of her room. Only, there is no going to her room this time. There will never be any more going to her room at any time. Swift depart. Does she, at this point, repair to her room? Stand and look out at me, diminished by distance? A tumblerful of honesty at her breast. See me unmoved, shaken to the core. Absorbing it all, taking nothing in. Slowly putting the pieces back together.

Of what? That? Irreparable.

Walk the Crags, looking for a spot to leap from. Insofar as I can look. Mind swimming, eyes intermittently clouded. Harbour doubt that the fall will kill. But kill it will, I know it. And not the revenge they'll claim. They – the non-suicides. Simply unable to bear the pain. No, not pain. The speed of the mind and the steep descent of the spirit. Call it that. Now that she's gone. But seeking a spot, a spark of interest. What rock is that?

Why can't the mind stay attuned? Even to its own destruction? Or is that why? So as not to be destroyed? Dolorous among the dolerite, I think. And you don't pun before you leap.

I'm safe.

Always knew it would come round again. Father the first. A big hole but fill it I did. All the time lurking, though. Hunched gnomishly on the branch. One word and on me at a bound. I always knew it would. With what? A mother a wife a son a daughter a career. Sir, I have been expecting. What word? Latterly lover. Over.

You touch a face and it's gone. Or you don't touch a face and it's still gone. Or the face changes. Expands like a map unfolding. You visited here and here, but not here. And now you never will. This place on the face that you never visited will not be here any more. For you to touch. I have divined this. Through a fog of my own devising.

No more I.

19

Dreaming like a beast these nights. Surprised each morning by the appearance of the eyes. Immediately attempts to restore a twinkle. Laughable. But the mirror doesn't lie. Apart from the one big lie of reversing all. Let's face it, reality can't be looked at. Not in the eye. Not with these eyes. Baggy and dark might seem sophisticated to some. To whom? Margaret from Finance for one. Only woman noticing at present. O Ruth, what a falling off was there. Is here. Meet me in the middle.

Octopus's Garden once again. For Marianne. The child's obsessed. Only has it on vinyl, so must lift and reposition the arm by hand. No such thing as repeat. Old enough to do it herself, but he is particular. Studies the cover, as ever, and asks him again to name them. Ringo, Paul, George, and John. Looking down the stairwell at EMI. Years apart.

- So they looked like this in 1967?

- No, it must have been taken earlier, much earlier.

- And then they looked like that in 1970?

- Yes, I think so.

- They're not doing it right.

- What do you mean?

- The second one is showing much more of his arm in 1970.

- That's Paul.

- And the first and the third ones are smiling like they did in 1967.

- Looks more like 64, 63.

- But the second and fourth ones aren't smiling at all in 1970.

- It wasn't so cool to smile in 1970.

- And they are all wearing the same clothes in 1967, but only two are wearing the same clothes in 1970.

- It wasn't so cool to wear the same clothes in 1970. It's probably just chance that two of them did.

- And the balconies look different.

- That's true. The two photographs are taken from slightly different angles.

- But why?

- It's hard to repeat things exactly as they were.

- No it's not.

Her head in the grass. Strands of her hair intertwined with it. The red and the green. No, more strawy. Autumn time. The big moon up in the blue. He is remembering himself remembering. The high rise on the horizon. Tall enough to leap from. To have had that thought even then! Even in the midst of. But the high rise vanishing, his hands slipping. Welts will be the next thing. And none to tend to him here. He didn't think of that. He couldn't possibly have been expected to think of that. He who prided himself on thinking of everything. We all know what that precedes. It won't be pretty, not like her head in the grass, that's guaranteed. Never did care about bystanders. Only the principals, who will be spared this surely. Christ, identification! Somebody close standing over him. Let it not be she.

Cats like ear wax. This one's mad for it. Let in when no one's around, which is nearly never. Only because he is so seldom there. Doubtless the house falls silent. Maybe the attic clock starts up again then. Ghost batteries. He likes the thought, lingers on it while the cat on his lap licks his right ear-finger. A house with curtains draped around. Widowed. Houses more like people than cats are. Streets have personalities. Some disordered, even. This cat clearly lunatic. Even a hollowed-out moon in the blue, seen through blinds. Curtains only in memory. Tried to explain to Roger once but couldn't. Except to say the moon was always there. Like God? Yes, a bit like God.

Watch over this cat, Lord. The neighbour's but one. Neglectful. Must be a story there. Must be stories everywhere. Let them run riot. It all comes down to this shrouded house now. In the middle of the day. Of the working day. Rare escape. To live a moment outside time. To sit and feed the cat ear wax. The neighbour's but one.

He needed that.

Breakdown in a chapel, of all places. Shouldn't have to witness that. Bad timing too, seeing as they are such irregular attendees. He says they. Rosemary a no-show. Staunch unbeliever. Himself worse than a waverer since the age of twelve. So why go? He who shall teach the Child to Doubt / The rotting Grave shall neer get out. Haunted by the lines. Actual horror of the sealed coffin, allied to misgivings regarding the scientific method. Odd for a man in his position. But doubt isn't the child's remit, he has observed that much.

- Why won't you let me sleep?

Screamed – no, barked – as she lunges at the Mary-statue. At communion time too. Watched as if in slo-mo. Half expecting the statue to move to shield itself. A miracle! Or a hammer to be produced, as with the Pietá in St. Peter's Basilica. Rosemary not so staunch that she didn't want to see it. A geologist, that one. No evidence of expertise in this attack. Patchwork skirt suggesting poverty at least. Insomnia a given. The unctious passkeeper tries to lead her away. Requires the assistance of three burly members of the congregation in the end. Slight impulse to help, but mercifully a sinner so always takes a pew to the rear. Added to the distance, uncertainty over whom to help. The woman? Let her lunge again? A fleeting notion. Though he has a geologists's hammer at home.

Marianne grips his hand, Roger his arm. That's the miracle.

Soup is all. Wants to get off now. A business lunch but the business no good. Three kindly ladies, perched in a row. Not much custom here. Somebody didn't do their homework. Corporate sounding but an office up a back alley. Cramped at that. He can't be expected to do everything. They are onto children now, he could melt hearts on the subject. Buttons his lip though. They don't ask. So sober today, he may appear childless. Well, let them conjecture. Or not. Feels himself irremediably dull, not often that happens. Could slip through the wall like a ghost. Like a dull ghost. Thinking this and catches eye of one. As she wipes the corner of her mouth. With the corner of her serviette.

She saw.

Didn't see that coming. Call from the Head, Rosemary said.

About Roger. Kicked a boy violently in the groin.

- Did you do it? I don't need to ask that. *Why* did you do it?

- I don't want to talk about it.

- I know you don't *want* to, but you will.

- He was slagging me off.

- What for?

- My name.

- What's wrong with your name?

- What's wrong with it? Roger? You do know what that means?

- It means famous with the spear.

- Why did you have to give me that name?

- It's a good name. It was your grandad's name.

- Nobody's called Roger any more.

- You are.

- I wish I wasn't.

- Just because some wee nyaff mocked you?

- He's not wee.

- So he's bigger than you?

- Yes.

- Well, that's something.

- You're not cross with me?

- I'm cross that you don't like your name.

- I do like it.

- Your mum says you made the boy's willy bleed.

- He had to go to the nurse. She put an ice pack on it.

- Poor bastard.

- Dad!

Mother in her Sunday best on a Saturday. The whole clan gathered. Wishing her many happy returns, but can there be? She says not one word to Rosemary all evening. When coats being put on and cars started, she sidles up to him.

    – Did you see that? That wife of yours? She never once looked the road I was on.

Microsoft, so tread softly. That's one account he doesn't want messed with. Should shake the place up a bit. Bawl what? Get my best people on it! I am my best people, he thinks. Cairns thinks so too. Went a bit pale when he heard, which was nice to see. Just a small offering to begin with, if it is just a beginning. This could make the difference. Between *here* and *there*. The title already got. *Micro*SOFT Skills in the Workplace. Delivered by comPRENDE e-learning. For research, a pint with Hannigan in the Griffin. And to crow.

Business is *busy*ness, Kendal can wait. Not possible this year, or the next, if all goes to plan. This he doesn't say.

    – But the kids! We should take them while we still can. It won't be long till we're persona non grata with them.

    – Personae non gratae.

    – Smart arse.

He'll miss the hills, in truth. That hanging mist. Descends and you can wade through it. To some thatched pub. Can't understand aversion to warm beer at all. Not exactly Anglophile, but no phobia to speak of.

    – I've always liked holidaying in England, he says. It feels different from here.

    But not this year.

Has taken to walking the lane of late. He says the lane.

Winds more or less in a circle past the park gates. Streetlit. Irritating for Rosemary as he is hardly home to begin with. Helps him to sleep, he says.

- Helps you to fall asleep maybe. But your apnoea has got worse.

- It's only snoring.

- There speaks a man.

The sleep claim bogus, of course. Lies awake longer into the night. Well, patchily, hence the snoring. Thinking of Ruth and if she thinks of him. He could find out, but that would be fatal. Space she needs above all. Not that she used that word. But he knows he does it, makes an open space feel enclosed. Overbearing, at times. Not many relish freedom. Worked for him in the past. Witness Rosemary. But Ruth different. Wanted to emerge from her own shadow, never mind his. This closer to her words. For some reason her voice fading, while all else stronger. Such as even her smell. Keep hold of that! Till the next pool of light.

Accepted reluctantly. Tried never to get too close to colleagues, romance apart. Even then. And Cairns only a sparring partner really. Would miss him, all the same. He will never have to.

Margaret from Finance. Difficulties with her daughter, she says. He has one too.

- Marianne's only *nine*, Margaret.

Still. She'd appreciate it.

Brings a bottle of red and a bottle of grape juice. Never known Margaret to drink, but she does. The daughter has the juice.

Quite unexceptional throughout. Till dessert, when told to fetch her drawing for him. Not a whit put out, as even Marianne would be. And even Marianne capable of better. Boats in the harbour, topped by a frowning sun. He can see that the boats are copied from the table mats.

– I like the sea best of all, he says.

She puts it away and they tuck into their crème caramel.

Excuses himself finally.

– You have a delightful daughter, Margaret, he says at the door.

– She was delightful tonight. Not normally.

– Well, it's a start.

– Yes, and it proves a theory I have. Thank you for going to all this trouble. I won't ask again.

– It was no trouble.

– No, that's not true, Martin. A man in your position can't be seen fraternising with someone from Finance.

– We are *all* Finance, Margaret.

– Watch your waist, she says.

Can hardly respond with first thoughts. She having steadily thickened since Marianne. Oddly not after Roger. Three years between the two. Three years of fitness regimes in front of the telly. Attractive still, all the same. Ageing not gracelessly, as some. Suits a fuller face, not that he can say. She can say, though. Out of concern for his health. Not good for you around the middle, it's true. History of heart disease in the family. And cancer, if that's relevant. It is if you have it. Knows she's right, too. Not exactly comfort eating, but the fast food van outside the office can't possibly help. The sooner they move from that estate, the better. Awful to bring clients there. Has tried the Hilton on occasion, but nobody's fooled. Unless they want to be. For as long as it takes to eat lunch. Longer. So there's that too. But the van the main culprit. Rosemary can't remember the last time she cooked for him. Weekends excluded, and not always then. So he takes a tape and the full-length mirror into the bathroom. As if it mattered. As if to fit himself up. For what?

Wave retracement in the sea, pine cone patterns, light refraction angles, petal formations on flowers. Lyricism of technical analysis, this is what people miss. They think he must be a hard nut to crack. When in fact.

Cairns notices eventually.

– You always keep the good stuff for yourself.

– The good stuff?

– The poetry.

Can't argue with that. Or with volume falling across the pattern and surging on the breakout. Twenty-minute lessons, the length of the human attention span. Wonders what it is for apes. An argument to be had for lessening the time to ten. He has had that argument with Hannigan, who is all for.

– Things have gone wrong since our day, Martin.

In truth, Hannigan only vaguely interested. An IT man in the end, so deals in nanoseconds, he supposes.

The IT generation. Parental deficiencies carried forward for each period. Ha!

No, you can see that the flag slopes against the prevailing trend. Flags. Triangles. Pennants. There is no poetry in money, the poet of the Far House had said. Who never knew about this.

Working all hours. So much so, Rosemary has quizzed him suspiciously. Yet never batted an eyelid the whole time with Ruth. Making himself unpopular in the office. Nobody able to sneak off early now. Cairns the most offended, as people management his job, he says. Discovering a new harshness in himself. Building the company up. Taking over the day-to-day stuff he knows he shouldn't. Writing again. Whole courses. Casts a withering eye on others' prose. Even sacked the copyeditor. First sacking of anyone on the team. The team! Kept missing Americanisms. Hardly a hanging offense. Couldn't do it until a client threatened action. A tribunal otherwise. Spared Cairns the task too. Got no thanks for that.

– What's the boy going to do with himself now?

Yes, a boy was right. Ridiculous blush on his face when he told him. Particularly violent on the neck. Had to look away eventually. He who always looked too long at everything. Uncomfortably long at everything.

– He doesn't know any better, he's African.

All eyes turn. On him.

As if a career built on knowledge and sophistication could vanish in an instant. Luckily just a few friends. One an Israeli Jew, another a Swede. Still. Meant in a kindly way, joking, can he say that now? For God's sake, it's only a game of football.

Blame the fervour of extra time, the copious single malt. A rash tackle and a red card for Bobo.

A European final too. First in thirty-three years.

– Guinean, I think. French-born.

Cairns chirps up.

– You didn't write the course on discrimination in the workplace, did you, Martin?

20

Here's Hannigan. Paper under one arm. Other flapping like a chicken wing. Flashed smile not returned. Heart pounding now. A second before it's said, he knows. He knew.

He knew, he knew, he always knew.

- Ruth's dead, Martin.

He wouldn't have. Not like that. Hasn't the nerve. Hadn't. Much too brutal. Goes past the old infirmary. To her street. Lonsdale Terrace, he can see the sign. Looks up at her room. At what once was her room. It didn't happen there, she didn't do it there. But he sees it there. Sees also bridges in the snow. Can't think why. Looks up at other windows. Sees a bare light bulb in one. And its shadow.

This is nowhere. Only thought. He is in these places without the advantage of a vantage point. As if he had consented to walk among the living. Consent not in it in the slightest. As if to beseech. Panic that he may not again be apart from all that. That he may be condemned to live it all again. Without, eventually, the sensation of being alive. But this isn't all. This is very far from being all. Parts missing, he cannot think of them now. In the same place in the same skin unable to alter anything. Separated from experience only by thought, as in the old days. Not a thing new under the sun. Some things different though. Or are they so? Not merely the blips of discontinuity? Only surprise the order. Surprise! Order! These are words to hang onto. In lieu of perch.

One letter left. Her last. Destroyed the rest to keep from prying eyes. More the kids' than Rosemary's. Doubts she'd be looking. Hid so well he cannot find it. Then does. Asks himself where his glance fell when he entered. Didn't fall, it rose. To the clock. That keeps the time no longer. Too loud a tick. Perched still like a barn owl above his books. Overflow from study once. Small chamber inside. Her roundish but not childish handwriting. Blue of the envelope reminds him of something. Wavy lines of the postmark, like strands of her hair across the stamp. Sent it to the office like a good girl. Discreet, she could be that. Finally not. Never lost the habit of opening his own mail. Self-reliance, Rosemary liked that in him. Not she. You can rely on me. Reads differently now. Reads please rely on me. Destroy this too. Too much like evidence now. Against. Folds to put in pocket, touches wet. Battery acid. Laughably thinks tears for a second. Hers, not his. As if all these years undried.

Taxi for him. Not a moment too soon. Palpitations again. Pit-a-pat. He whose even temper is famed. In such circles as he moves. Not a mystery, really. After the month he's had. Still, get it checked out. That quack Barrett. Valium, perhaps. Prescribed for his mother in the bad old days. No, that was the father. Same portly appearance. After the priest, the doctor. Certified all dead in time. All the blessed dead. Calming down already. Driver's eyes quizzical in the mirror. Must have a haggard look. Hangdog, he's seen it himself. Not to worry. A taxi a confessional. No driver breaks the seal. Or if he does, you don't get to hear. You again. No, impersonal that time. Impersonal is best, as always.

He is hearing this now. He is allowed this now. After a prolonged period of what you may call deafness. The single malt helps. Copiously. Staring into the dark. Her voice like water. Lap it up. Might have warned him with it. Without it. Maybe did. The cold calls. Naturally, those! Shiver now you say it. Oh you is allowed now, it seems. To be used against him. When *he* sees fit. When *he* sees fit then *you* will be used against him. I am interrupting my enemy, he thinks. Anything to bury the day.

Into the dark. Isn't it the best place to be, after all? Before nothing. Something she knew. Might have warned him. Might have spoken to him. They had a date. First of August seven years from now. Not contractually obliged to free himself till then. Might have written or called. Sought his opinion. His affection. Never lost that.

Fibrillation. Needs an eye kept on it. Atrial, not ventricular. Not fatal. Or could be fatal in combination with other factors. None such, happy to report. At risk of stroke, but keep healthy and stress at bay. Anything panicking him? Then simply keep an eye on. No harm in improving it. No harm in that either, if it's not too rigorous. See it in men in their fifties more commonly, but not a surprise. Aspirin may help. Warfarin. But not yet. Monitor for a bit. Saw his mother the other day. Said he was third generation of his family she'd been a patient of. Spoke about grandfather's practice. Nice story about him arranging to see woman with awful skin disease last. To save embarrassment, she said. Didn't want to ask whose. Definitely nothing worrying him? Sorry, it's atrial fibrillation. A-fib for short.

- Old Bill just called.

 - What about?

- I didn't ask.

- Why not?

- I thought it might be private. You know. Money worries.

- Who's worried about money?

- I'm sorry. I just thought, Old Bill's the man to go to.

- I haven't *gone to him* in about ten years.

- I know. Which is why I wondered.

- Well, don't wonder.

- Don't be so bloody crabbit. Will I call him now?

- Why? You short of cash?

- Oh fuck off, Martin.

Myra Hindley. How's that for an opening gambit? Regards the girl in the light of the bar. Not a girl. In close proximity, but having to edge closer to engage. She to him. Bit of a sparkle in the eyes. Has said umpteen times eyes meeting and sparkling never happens. Does now. Flattered, all the same. Hannigan will look ceiling-wards if he walks in now. She is a sweet wine breath away. Says she thinks it criminal this talk of release.

- She deserves to rot for what she did.

- It doesn't half get the wind up people though, he says. Nothing like infanticide to unite the nation.

She recoils, visibly, he sees it with his own eyes. The sparkle only in her drink now. A bit extreme there. And to accomplish what? Why? What's happening to him? What happened?

Hare Krishna. At the foot of the Playfair Steps. In her blue robes, if they are such. Lovely freckled face. Lets her accost

him. Where's the harm? Talk about consciousness. Has a
leaflet about it, a tin can too. Simple begging. He gets angry
about that. Inside. Wanting to awaken her. He recounts the
story of her entanglement, as he imagines it. The emptiness
that needed filled. The bad translations of the Gita and
other Penguin Classics that filled it. Her hurt look. Painful
now to see.

- You started off being nice, she says, but then you got nasty.

Shame as she turns aside. Simple sweep of her blue
robes, if they are such. Onto the next accost. He left with
egg on his face. And the horror.

- I must confess.

The ashtray is spinning. As are the pictures on the wall.
As is his head. Motoring home after a conference, a roadside
cafe in the night. This woman. Not long at the firm, didn't
stay much longer. Passing through. Though must have
entertained hopes for her. Not those sort. Holy smoke. Her
words lost among it. What must she confess? That it had
bored the pants off her? Not like that at all. The pictures
of bridges in the snow, these have made it across. A bit arty
for a cafe. Doesn't she think? Confessing to her philistinism,
that's it. A bit of a philistine, is what she says. When it comes
to art. Hardly art. Still. Confess.

Never you mind. Gauging size of Rosemary's plans for the
big day. The bigger her plans for him, the bigger his plans
for her. Hers after his. Gemini both, as luck would have it.
Compatible. A large parcel in the hall. She can't move it
by herself and he can't help her. Put a throw over for now.
Couldn't stand to have a joint celebration. Nothing like that
since their wedding. And the christenings. No, Marianne's
low key. Nothing like that since Roger's christening. And

their wedding. Unhappy birthday, for her. For him, hollow. Still, can't be a misery. Smile all the while. Rosemary cannot, though she tries. Awful business with the roses, won't make that mistake twice. Singing's not going to help at all, is it? That's the time you must keep on trying. Though you're nothing but a basketful of lies.

Ein brauner Baum. Better in German, rounder and deader. A brown tree. Not to be mistaken for a green tree. One fit to hang from. Sees it in the yard. Whose? Ah yes, his German aunt's. Second wife, no better than the first. Of course he will stay for supper. Love for his wife and children to visit, they both would. Ten and thirteen. Doesn't it just? Only the wolf dogs for company now. Lonely. If only! Uncle shouldn't be long in Rothenburg, some business with wood. A terribly dry summer. Look at the tree in the yard! Could happily hang from it, like the penitent zealot. Be the strange fruit of the song. Whither thou goest, I will go. Ein brauner Baum. A brown tree.

Bury the day. Under so many headlines. Say one. Abu Ghraib Report Faults Rumsfeld. Impossible to check veracity, or choose the sports pages. Can see only his own eyes follow the newsprint. Movement lateral and downward. Unless they look up. Yes, caught a flicker there. Up at the ceiling. Like the spy trial of Alger Hiss, called out as a psychopath for doing same. Not following proceedings. Looking up at the ceiling. According to Karl Bing or Binger, a famous psychiatrist. Till the defense attorney upped and spoke. 'Your Honor, you will notice that Dr Binger is looking at the ceiling.' Binger is right. Alger Hiss a name to reckon with. Sees it now there in the newsprint. Alger Hiss Remark Faults Binger. Under a picture of his attorney. Who upped and spoke, upped and spoke. Your Honor.

He stands accused. No, he is seated, on the worn lime-green sofa. Not enough time to place this in time. A dream, clearly. It seems he is allowed this. This once. Accused of what? It doesn't seem to matter, all think him innocent. All bar one. Mother? He rails against her. A man in a white suit appears, attempts to smooth things over. Says there is no doubt he is innocent, but he should reflect on why she suspects him. Because he *has* been guilty of wrongdoing in the past. Of what exactly? Wrongdoing. When exactly? In the past.

21

His father's saw. Rust right the way along its teeth. All that remains. No angle grind, chisel, spirit level, or Dremel. His mother's doing. Not even the coal scuttle they were kept in. But the saw he salvaged. Hung on a nail in the cupboard under the stairs. Hid from view. Old coats primarily. At moments of great stress he clears a space in the cupboard and regards his father's saw. Does so now, parting the coats with his hands. Thinks, her body will be like this too one day. Friable.

Under the standard lamp's pool of light, reading, not really reading, listening. For it to ring again. He sees himself make the short walk to pick up. Listening differently. Waiting on a word, a snigger. Kids up at this hour. Are there no Walls in your house? But the silences! Somehow lingering.

He is crossing the road with Hannigan, looking left. Amsterdam tram headed for the Dam. Part work, part jaunt Rosemary is fine with. A few Trappist beers inside them.

   – We stopped at the kerb, but maybe in another existence we kept on walking.

   – How many universes would you need to accommodate every possibility?

– An infinite number.

– And you think this is possible?

– It's a theory. You taught me it.

– Did I?

– The multiverse theory.

– That's right. William James proposed it. I used to read those boys.

– I often think about it.

– Isn't it enough just to imagine what might have been?

– There's a word for that. Regret.

Any port in a storm. In the bandstand with the jakeys while the rain falls. Their crap patter. Fingering a brooch picked up near the hydrangeas. Not to give. On impulse. And now must get shot of. Lest Rosemary rifle through his pockets. Hark at him! Become almost routine now. Divesting himself of the evidence. When clearly no need. Witness the state of his health. Expansiveness of movement. His breathing freely on the hill. Sure signs subterfuge on the wane. Never gone fully, that would be death. He supposes. Feels in his pocket the brooch missing its stone. Pokes the tip of his pinkie through.

If he had kept it he might have braved Hades.

Don't cry at the football. Cardinal sin to, but can't help himself. Wipe it away. Nothing on the park. On the terraces. Na, na na, na na na, na. Coda to Hey Jude. On the radio the first time he broke down. After his dad. Held it together till then. Never knowingly played it since. And now from the terraces. That aren't terraces any more. When cruising deftly to victory. Has to be magic in the air for them to sing it. The floodlit night air. Never was one for the masses, but make an exception. The terraces. No man can be more innocently employed. Belting out the coda to Hey Jude. That aren't terraces any more.

It seems he is allowed this. One moment of grace. Under a tree with a transistor radio. Out of sequence. Must have come to mind in the time he is now. Elmore James singing it hurts me too. Under the green foliage of he knows not what. Never got around to getting the big book on trees. Why lick up behind him? And take his mess? Slide guitar for the feelings to glide on. Tenderness towards an unfaithful one, blinded himself to it for obvious reasons. Tried not to pick up on the signs. Known only too well from his own doings. And leavings. Can't begrudge her that. Must have worked out badly for her. Unexpected sympathy. Only to be expected, he could never bear the kids haranguing her. Actually could not bear it. If he had cultivated that side everything would have been different. Useless to think. Think what Elmore James knew. Out with his dogs in the woods. Drowning in Mississippi moonshine. Relayed to beneath a tree somewhere-nowhere. A young man and his radio. The same man older, hurt, then older still, and falling. Recalling his own doings. And leavings.

In the doorway late at night. Elbows up with Hannigan at the Griffin. Got chatting with a Palestinian girl. Told him God baked man just right in the Middle East. First attempt too black, second attempt too white. Hannigan had the hots for her, so he left him to it. To her. Knowing he would do nothing. In truth, stirred. Felt it as he got up to go. Now almost reaches the bus station when he sees one. Emerge from the shadows, as they say. Want business, she says. Dark drugged eyes. Somewhat like. Though she never on any medication. Saw too much of that, she said. Yes, eyes like hers, only lifeless. Nearly lifeless. But same dark inward. Same dark intoxicating inward. Drinking a pool of light.

His photo in the paper. One for the album nobody keeps. This a first. If you exclude crowd scenes. Student demonstrations in his political days, don't laugh. Business Gets Creative. Artist Sara Down teams up with Martin Prendergast, Director of *com*PRENDE *e-learning*. Nice girl, bit scatty. Made a Tree of Knowledge installation for the office. Much shredding involved. Doubts they'll take it with them, if they do ever leave. He with heart-attack face, she as brown as a nut. Must be the way ink's absorbed by newsprint. Distorted quote too. Had lamely called it an educational experience. This became he had learned a lot. Keep it simple. Madness to have got involved. Liked being around artists once. Couldn't risk an evening class again. A mousy girl, this one. Still. Kept the temp on her toes. Keen to show what real work was. Priceless puzzled look.

Office mess. Must be the cowboy accountant's. It is a good joke, an accountant in cowboy boots. Extraordinarily pointed toes too. Couple of files levelling the table legs, trusts one isn't his. Accountant to the stars, he laughs. Miracle there's never been an audit. Feels oddly obligated to him now. For steering him past the early-days booby-traps. No start-up less savvy than he then.

- The older I get, the less I think of bank robbery as a crime. No, really, it is almost a duty to rob one. Before our wives shuffle off their intrauterine coils, just you and me, swag bags and the open road, what d'you say?

- Who'd be Bonnie?

- I was thinking more Frank Gardner and Ben Hall, 1860s' New South Wales. All that lovely gold.

Laughter. Laughter like sea spray in the sun.

Turn then, most gracious advocate, thine eyes of mercy towards us.

A shiver as he strokes the spine. Lifts to his nose.

Old-lady must. A wonder it hasn't crumbled to dust. As she.

Canon Plunkett pasted on one page. General Michael Collins on another.

For the repose of the soul of.

Who will want this when he goes? Not Rosemary. Not Marianne.

That's death for you, real death. Where no one cares.

And after this our exile.

Perhaps they'll give it to his mother. It was her mother's prayerbook after all. Before nothing. Reunite the two. Like mother like daughter.

Who will resemble him? Roger his own man already. Never did take a leaf out of his book.

The leaves of this one coming loose.

Should have put it in the ground with her.

Her red hair clear as day. If he had only kept some. Never was that sort. Kept her letters for a bit, but with kids you can't. Burrow into everything. Used to remember parts by heart. Only stray phrases now. You mustn't think that. If anyone could. Can pick out a speck of red in any crowd. Landscape, even. The exact tinge. Sees it fringed on the pillow clear as day. Always was day. The shutters couldn't hide that.

Time enough to resume. Would have to retrain, get her

registration again. No need to be at home. Who needs convincing here? Talk it through night after night, glass after glass. Truth is, never loved nursing. As such. The psych ward the last straw. Men without hope. Money tight but they could do it. They did do it. Reaped the rewards. And now? Vista of nothingness and panic in the night. Time enough to resume. Or if not that, something else. Ancient Celtic women had professions. Is that supposed to help?

A break in the Catskills. Or jaunt across the Mendips. Feeling the need of peaks suddenly. Rosemary on the other hand need only climb under the sheets. Understandable as her own mother never reached forty. Unhappy birthday. Poor woman, framed on the bed by red roses. Some man her dad! Could have gone the other way, of course. Given her a new lease of life. So he had hoped. Still, may not last. Once she is over the hump. Just the prospect of her fifties to scare her then. Out of her wits. Let that sink in. Oh God, alone.

Prank calls plaguing them at an end. Is Mr Walls in? Wouldn't have minded that. But the silences! Still going when you picked up again. Rosemary said not to listen, but he did. Couldn't help himself. Convinced he could hear breathing, then conceded it was his own. Cold calls gone wrong, apparently it happens. Just as you sit down to dinner. Not these. Always only at night. The children asleep. Rosemary would pick up, then after midnight he. At an end now. Then why is he listening?

They beat a path to his door. In their hoods again. He is there in the happy light. The kitchen light condensing on the dew. He smiles at a word. That can't be heard. He on his favourite stool. Regarding one who enters. Regarding another who leaves. Glancing up at the clock at times. Not really taking it in. The time. That time. He lifts the plate, a hand reaches out. The window-dark made darker by the light. Begins to oppress him. He glances there too at first. Then ceases. Neck stiffens. As they beat a path to his door.

The hooded sorrows.

22

Finds it in her dookit. Hard to believe at first. Then feels a small fool suddenly. For presuming he was ever enough. Not she for him, but he for her, apparently. Only not. Never too soon to learn. Moulded almost identically from the clay, I the same dirt as you. Let's not fool ourselves. There we have it, ladies and gentlemen. Leaks in air everywhere, which somehow have got to be plugged. With delightful counterfeits. Just when he had resolved to be true too. Root out her despond.

Right so.

Meaning it will be harder than he thought. As hard as this.

The shape universe or he is nowhere at all. Those bright boys could well have been on the money. Time does not exist, but if he hangs around for long enough it will. Impact of some sort inevitable. Hard not to concede inevitability when you are a few feet from death. Time only an accumulation of certain distances between certain impacts. The longest hundred miles, such is life. With a score by Franz Waxman.

Looks at his watch twice to check not dreaming. Mind poor at picking up sequence in dream. Aghast that the face is cracked and the hands stopped. Is he dead already? It can't be. First because he feels intensely the pressure of moving at speed. Second because the sensation of being alive is so familiar to him that he could not mistake it. The time of thought is not the time of time. The same pressure being applied to his hurtling body may have cracked the face and stopped the hands. If, indeed, the hands have stopped at all. For is he not watching for movement in an interval when only minimal movement occurs? Too slight to be discerned. By the naked eye. No eye more naked than his now. But not the body naked. This is not a dream.

– You never buy me flowers.

Age-old reproach. Cuts him to the quick because true. Or only time he did was after each reproach. Once a decent interval had elapsed. So as not to seem forced or as if under her thumb. A week, say, ten days at most. From Simply Flowers. A bell rings as the door opens. An actual bell. Not knowing the names, or knowing the names but forgetting suddenly. Absurd. Asks for purples and whites, but not lilies. Made the mistake of a dozen red roses once. Roses mean death to me, she said. Her mother had lain surrounded by them. Some man her dad! But he thinks of flowers now without need of reproach. To bring a spark of life to doleful eyes. My Rosemary. Oddly suits despond. Purple and white her colours.

– You bought me flowers.

It can't be done. That's the spirit. Let it all go to pot. He put these shelves up nearly twenty years ago. *Before* Roger. His study, where he never could, became the baby room too soon. Not as anticipated or decorated for. Sudden change of heart. A new mother's heart unfathomable, best not to try. So the boy grew, overlooked by Camus. Neat little foreign fiction shelf. Couldn't bear to load the wood with guff. The Golden Age of Capitalism, store that away. And now all leaning. The wood sapped of its vigour. Make a fresh start. Not on my watch. Keep as is, as was. When he could soothe his son while reading Mother died today. Or maybe yesterday, I can't be sure.

Marianne is walking through the park. Towards him. He sees her see him and then blush. She is with a friend. On some assignation, perhaps. A female friend. Hard to tell in this dark but doubtless Mary-Jo. Separated at birth, he always says. He who missed the main event those years ago. She turns to whisper. Only a bluff to cover her blush. Embarrassed why? That her father should exist in a place she never expected. On some assignation of his own, perhaps. In a public park. Where the ducks are. And the boys who follow you till you chase them away. With a cutting word. Or stay on your tail till you re-enter the light. Or even afterwards. But not with your father with you. Who has just attended a political meeting. To shoot the breeze with a comrade or two. For old time's sake. None remaining. Not the Trotskyites with their little missals. Fellow travellers. Her blush unseen. In a public park. Inferred.

Not to sleep. Imperative, he tells himself. On this slippy pole. He who never used the word imperative. That is different, then. Odd if this look-back occasioned a change. And how look back on that? Endless ramifications. Like the magazine cover of the man holding the magazine cover. Or put another way. His presence here accelerates the change. Yet not catalysis. A catalyst as everyone knows is not consumed. Unlike him. If we care to observe.

The more he craves the lighter love is. In the light the

longing checked. Looking through a hole in light the dark. Ah dark the glamour of that but light the source. In truth in lies in light in dark. The less he craves the darker light is. Never was a look he looked for but came out of the blue. The look she had the light she wore. The love he craves is waiting for him somewhere.

Why so much ooze from that? Oh he is slipping now. Now he is in another place. A garage of some description. Describe it, then. No time. First there is time, then there is no time. A large freezer. Lid on top. Already open. Open for a while, by the look of things. Must be half a cow in there. Wholly thawed. Hears a voice from the yard. Somehow he knows there is a yard. Not yet placed the place. A shrill voice. A voice he knows, but doesn't understand. Jesus, yes, his German aunt's. They've cut the power, his uncle explains. In the night. Those hooligans. Dad's brother, last of that line. Never came back from Berlin. Postwar reconstruction. Living in the hills now. With his second wife. Where you'd think they'd have peace. Rosemary couldn't make it. Or the children. He shows the photographs. But the eyes dim, and wandering.

Hooligans! Hängen ist zu gut für sie.

McCloud on horseback in Manhattan. Ancient repeat. All lined up on the sofa, Roger's girlfriend of a week at the edge of it. Gripping. Posh crisps and Tizer. Family viewing. Rosemary indulgent. Must be something better than this on. Tanya, would you like? Tanya would like. Dust down the anecdotes. Origin of Roger's aversion to butter. Explaining the foot-shaped hole in the toilet door. The poor girl laughing like a drain. Like a nervous drain. Roger showing little enthusiasm, then none. Almost having to kick the pair upstairs.

- I think that went well.

Resists the new girl. It should get easier with age. Doesn't. Not that he is a hound. Couldn't stand to have meaning involved again, well and truly did for him, but casual not really his thing either. And then, of course, trouble if you let them go. Tribunals and the like. Make it into the paper. Might amaze the kids though. Daddy, we hardly knew you. Bit pathetic to be congratulating himself, all the same. For not responding to a prompt. Like some salivating dog. Like the hound he thinks he is, saying he is not. She was only playing along with his singing at the coffee station. Pour lil sugar on me. Hardly constitutes seduction. Except that she kept it up, longer than anticipated. Till he had to look away. He who always looked uncomfortably long. At everything.

Post! Even Rosemary up for this. In her dressing gown, but still. And time for coffee and toast together, as in the old days. An egg would be too much. Soldiers? Stop it. The envelope brown, as ever. Brown spells serious. Lets Rosemary take it up to her. He behind, a forlorn prince. Must be the Royal Mail put him in mind. Marianne sits up, fakes a yawn.

    - Well, open it.

    - Give us a chance.

    Not roughly torn, as with Roger. As with Roger, straight As, taken in at a glance. Kisses all round. Flinching from his, mother and daughter both. Just perceptibly. Still. A happy morning. The few remaining already gone.

What he thought a trunk is a pole. With a climbing plant entangling into knots. These he clings to. Knowing his hands will give. Seeming to excrete a kind of juice. A dew. A balm. Not a balm. Enough leaves for doubt but obscuring nothing. From view. It is a pole. He is on a slippery pole. This must mean it is ending soon. Soon to drop. And yet the scenes so mild. Not mild enough. Wishes he could see himself take her in his arms as in the old days. In open view of the kids. Behind her at the stove, is that word allowed? A gentle amused brush-off. If he opens his arms now he will know about it. Drop like a dead weight. Isn't that the idea? It is, and yet he clings. To the excreting knots. To see the mild scenes. A kind of palliative for the other ones. Milk as well as gall. Those that what? Excruciate. A kind of balm, then, after all. Before nothing. Hastening his descent. Hark at him now.

Seeing Roger through the glass of The Phone Shop. Slight blush on his face at the till. Never was good with money. Never taught him to be. Spent his own Uni summers unpacking fruit in Malcolm Campbell's. Has washed fruit religiously ever since. The only thing learned there. Notes in your pocket at last, that was the idea. Supplement his grant, his mother wouldn't. Dad a long time gone, it seemed. But he is here, watching his own son through the glass. Don't look up. Only to check on him, momently. Like he did last thing. Always. Bedding no sooner sorted than thrown off again. Never was a settled sleeper. That's all right. The mentally ill lie still. He read that somewhere, and it always stayed with him. Opposite of what you'd think, this appeals. Appeals because he always did do everything arse-over-elbow. His mum's words, naturally. Now his son who doesn't call and never was good with money works the till at The Phone Shop. All is well.

Palma airport in the midday sun. Flocks of tourists narrowing at the gates, then fanning out, preparing to disport themselves. He in sober attire for the symposium. Keynote speaker, expenses and a fee. Small enough but you have to do it. Educación a distancia. At a distance is right. Picks up his fiat and heads for the hills. The rocky road to Deia. Only to find the Far House locked. Still, he can stroll the garden. Olives, carobs, almonds, tangerines. Down to the picturesque graveyard. Not a soul in sight. Finds the grave uncannily quickly too. The famous dead. The chiselled letters like handwriting he recognises. Yes, just like hers, roundish but not childish. Just like it.

As you were. Phrase he had used in his lecturing days. As the hush descended. Well, it always descends, doesn't it? As if the oblivion we seek hovered over us. As you were. As much as to say, it's different with me, you can still chortle and nudge one another and pass notes and flirt. Just so long as there's enough quiet for me to be heard. Because what I am about to impart is worth receiving, and for your sakes, not mine. No ego here. Other than the kind of ego that announces itself by saying no ego here. Except this time it's Rosemary. In bed during the day with her hardboiled 'tecs. Can't begrudge her those. He has, does he not, his spaghetti westerns, Parolini, a box set. If You Meet Sartana Pray for Your Death. Return of Sabata. God's Gun. Little Johnny O'Hara riding off to Mexico to plead for help. Save our city. It's all there. As you were.

23

If he falters now he might catch himself.

On that first day. Hard hat on. They are putting the finishing touches. Strolls the perimeter. Call it that. He has no clue. Nods as if he has. Thirteen floors, so they would be dead centre. Smack dab in the middle. He is hearing all this, nodding at all this. Excited by the sales pitch. Unlike him. He could walk the stairs for exercise. Starting to need to. How many would that be? Say sixteen to eighteen in a flight, two flights per floor, twelve flights in all, that's a hundred-and-ninety-two to two-hundred-and-sixteen. Every second day, perhaps. The pitch stepped up since he stopped nodding.

– That's lucky.

    – I'll need Bill's shares though.

    – Why?

    – He doesn't deserve to do well out of this.

    – You couldn't have done any of it without him.

    – That's just what I tell him.

    – No. I was there. You couldn't have.

    – Well, the old dog's had his day.

- I'm not arguing. I didn't want you to go to him in the first place.

- You just said I couldn't have done it without him.

- You could have done some other thing.

- Then everything would be different.

Not any more with them. Would rather die first. Thus Marianne expressed herself. Thus they took themselves off. Back to the old jaunts and haunts. The places they first knew. Before anyone came out of them. Their loins. The old sandy beaches. Everything more tattered. Fewer boats in the bay. But the contours the same. The blue forgotten hills. Not entirely. That one a chicken in the oven, Roger said. They laugh again. Hard to laugh. Wish they hadn't gone here with them. Would rather live again, see their old jaunts and haunts again. Never having brought the children.

Night sweats, she says. The sheets always in the wash. And only sheets now. Can't stand to have a duvet over her. He on his side with a twice-folded blanket in addition. Always slipping off. Where is he now that he can see this? Over by the dressing-table mirror. Is he the mirror, then, reflecting it? No, he is not. For the avoidance of doubt, never is he animal, vegetable or mineral. Sees her stir and turn, stir and turn. Himself wake and stay. Till she is quiet again. All movement ceased. And that can be a while. By the clock? He forgot to look. Sees the red digits magnified by water. In the glass that is his nightly ritual. Never drunk from. His bladder incapable. So it goes. So the nights go. Off and on. Off and on.

Just a dip. No need to remove all. More than a paddle, though. Make you feel born again. Haha. See how green the water is. A wonder. Cold as hell, of course. Rosemary will regard him from the bathtowel. Or not. Has no need of inspection now. Flesh has no upward trajectory, so expands. In the middle. They are in the middle now. Rosemary on the bathtowel. A large-patterned affair. Colourful, in its way. She has the baby lotion on, he the screen. Careful in middle age. Cancer in the family. Watch out for the jellyfish, they abound here. The dead crab at his feet. Remembers Roger. First sight of death, on the beach. Let go his hand. The crab on its back. Inspected it. Looked up. Asked, Is it waiting for somebody?

The neighbour boy's birthday. Cute in his blue suit. Was Roger ever like that? Yes he was. They had a long wait, IVF perhaps, but you don't like to ask. Watched them visibly wilt over the hedge, as the hedge grew, as Roger and then Marianne rubbed in the salt. Marianne here today, suffering in body and spirit. Babysat him once upon a time. When the thought of being a nursery nurse was uppermost in her thoughts. As she relayed them then. As she did then. A game of pop the balloons. Tied to their ankles then their wrists. Cocktail sticks for weapons. Marianne melts a little, he sees it in her face. Amused eyes. All the more prized. She would like to take the boy in her lap. Stops herself. This he surmises. Her lap now reserved for others, she hopes. She fears. All this he surmises. The tall boys. Long since grown out of their blue suits. The awkward squad. Menacing, they suppose. You have to look away, for their sake. He who always looked too long. At everything. Uncomfortably long at everything.

Again this I, briefly. Troubled him since he can't remember. My I like your I, like everybody's I. So that is what binds us. Knowing what your I must be like but not feeling it is like never having been born. Or being dead. But how come *this* I? Which, what it must be like, others can know but not feel. And if it had never been? And if he ends it? If it had never been or if he ends it doesn't amount to a hill of beans. But whence it came? Can that be answered ere he does? End it, he means. Beans! Ere! Hark at him now, at the end of the day. Slip-ons slipped off. Desk blotter covered in sideways-eights. Tying himself up in knots and nots.

How do you entertain a corpse? In this office? Old Bill, Old dead-and-buried Bill. How to prise the shares out of him? Call him generous, for a start. Make his pitiful contribution an act of charity. What's twenty-five percent of nothing, Bill? You don't hoodwink old hawks like Bill too easily, with business booming. Only has to look around to see it. He hears it now. A comic-book exchange in his head.

- You were a chalk-and-gown man before I stumped up the cash.

- True, Bill, and I'm *grateful*. You know I am.

- I don't want gratitude, just a healthy return.

- That's what I'm offering, Bill. A healthy, a very healthy, return.

- It's not twenty-five percent of nothing now, you know.

- I know that, Bill.

- What's more, I'm *entitled*.

- Nobody more so.

- I thought I would just keep going.

- But you knew Roger was home.

- I thought he'd stay the night at least.

- Where? You've turned his room into a dump. Your dump.

- I'm sorry, love. I'll clear it out once the move happens.

- What move?

- To our new office.

- When did you plan on telling me this?

- I did tell you. Remember you said the seventh floor was lucky?

- Well, how am I supposed to remember everything, with so much going on?

- So much what? What's going on?

- Oh everything. *Everything.*

How did the ground get like this? The last time he looked, it was dry dirt, gravelly even. And now a shining parquet floor. Unreal. Linoleum, perhaps. He cannot feel it. He can feel it but not directly, not against skin. This isn't allowed, it seems. Marvellous if he could slip on it, have at least that sensation. This a new phase now. Unperilous. Best be on his guard, then. He who sniffed danger on the most scentless breeze. That's a good one. Turn him into an animal of some sort. Which would he care to be? Oh a jackal of course. Blessed be the jackal, he alone has the cure. On a fake parquet floor.

The business coasting, which is no bad thing. The danger now that pioneers become old hat, the young sharks move in. Not serious because knowledge is accumulated. Saw one calling itself Easy-Learning. They will see that off.

The proposed new logo, insight the brief. Opens it up and gasps. Audibly, apparently.

Above *com*PRENDE, an eye. An eye like a button on Rosemary's coat.

In Queen's Park for medicinal purposes. Walking with

Rosemary till her despond lifts. It doesn't. Joggers out in force, of course. Impervious to the place. To them. Jakeys by the bandstand, as they always are. Oh to punch their lights out. Tear up the peed-on primroses by the roots.

- It's a great view of the city.

- Yes.

- Marianne would love this.

- I asked her to come but she wouldn't.

- She's at a difficult age.

- So am I.

She buttons up her coat despite the heat. The buttons like gnarled eyes. Death symbols from a royal tomb. At Ur. He is breezy to the point of evanescence. Light where she is heavy. Vanishing point. Off of the face of the earth. Yet must be her rock.

- I am in chains, she says.

Defeated, he takes her hand.

Marianne a bit green.

- You'd go all that way for *him*?

He would and he'd go as far for you. The scowl of a cat made to look up from its dish. It will last another year. It did last another year, abating less than he'd imagined. Always a discontented child. Smiles all the more prized therefore. Glasses despite her perfect vision. He wouldn't understand. Irony is, a more studious look just as she has abandoned her studies. Rosemary says boys but you can't be sure. He checks the eyes for drugs, as his mother checked his.

- Dad, you're not listening.

He is listening all right. Every crabbit word like a kiss now, till dissolve. Such as she gave last thing, tucked in with Cottontail.

- Dad!

Stops off at a church with a golden Christ. Hanging crucified outside. Episcopalian. An anti-Roman notice on the board. Always liked churches, since belief left him. At the age of twelve. Thenabouts. Lights candles if he can. Can't have too much light. Or, where no candles, feels the grooves of the sill. Tests the pew. Too rigid. Standing ruminating in altarlight he can hear the traffic surf. Like his Gospel of St John with the photo of Rome. People hurrying about their day, in the rain, in see-through headscarves and macs. Short skirts, he can't help but notice. All too believable. He sits and says a prayer for his son.

Going up the road to check on Roger. His mother worried, naturally. They don't like this not coming home at term-end. Sends postcards but they are not enough. A four-hour drive, three if he hadn't taken the scenic route. As, in truth, he is unconcerned. Remembers his own time in the haze. No work done and the DTs, that was the life. Turns into the street. A burnt-out sofa on the lawn. He says lawn. Knocking repeatedly on the door. Till it opens on Roger, waist-up naked and bald as a coot. A party, apparently. Got a little out of hand. A wee bung to keep you going. When that grows back an inch, visit us.

24

In the annointed place. At the annointed time.

This he knows to be unreal. First of all, because they demolished the place. Second of all, because he entertains some hope that she will turn up. And this is not possible.

The dust inhaled by passers-by, seemingly uncaring. Legs intertwined under the picnic table like the surface roots. All muck and beerspill. And finally the beginning. Of it all. This time again. But not here. Not now. The lust exposed to passers-by, seemingly uncaring. But not here. Not now.

Shards of glass mixed with the shat-on tree roots. What are they building now? A municipal car park, perhaps. In the place where The Green Tree stood. In the place where they had sat, hands joined under the picnic table. At the unappointed time.

August. Of course it is. August the first. Put that on the desk. Of a searing heat before. Not now. Even the down-and-outs had their summer attire. This cheered him. He commented on it and this cheered her. But she is not here, she cannot be. He sees the bar and the stools, of course he does. Grandstand on the telly. No, that was then. A Saturday therefore. This not therefore. Thirteen years after the first. Because lucky thirteen, she said. Which was her all over. Can that be calculated? No, but looks like Wednesday. Or possibly Tuesday. Or possibly Monday. Horse racing. One jockey has her colour. Mary-mantle blue, he told her. Matching the eyes, you see. He sees. No, not yet. He left the blue above, he cannot see it now. Unless of course he turns in air. We'll meet again, she said. Bound to, he thought. So set it in stone. The day we met, she said. In The Green Tree. Thirteen years to the day. To the day or the date? To the date, then. Marvellous he can hear all this. Not that he does. He cannot hear her now. Mary-mantle at the starting gate. What were the odds?

18:11 the time. Day, month and year rolled into one. Clever of her. Arrived with not a minute to spare. He has none. Industrial clock on the wall, he likes that. Reassuring. Love set to time and motion. Apt as she was always leaving him to start her shift. In the Infirmary. He never ventured near. But he could see her, white tunic in the milky light. Dissolve.

Why is this allowed? This that never was? The place already gone. Because he had imagined it so thoroughly? He is allowed to visit his imagining, it seems. This one time. Not clever really to arrange to meet here. Hardly a landmark. Which had occurred to neither. Emotion running high, of course. But no scene. She in the saddle, directing. You go your way. How could it possibly be? If they had met before? But then she would have been a baby. He could have been a monk, left the monastery just in time. Hard to be a monk when you don't believe in God, as I don't, a monk had told him. Nice to picture her as a baby, with her just-given name having the ring of truth. What made them think The Green Tree would stand? Old and irrecoverable, that's the usual story. He had short-circuited time. Deceived it. Yet here it was, industrial hands intact. Time is the deceiver. And well you knew it.

Is this the end of the line? Only to here? All that rush only to loiter? A kind of desert station he knows will be demolished. No sudden impact. A guest room when the guests have gone. With the clock that tells the time. 18:11. Year of the Luddites. He must have known that then. He must have said that then. Apt when she was always leaving him. To smash up the place. The fire inside his even temper. He looks around wildly, wanting to smash up the place. Well, he'll have his wish soon.

At the end of the day he was married. A bit cut and dried, but that's what she liked, honesty. In a tumbler on her yellow window-ledge. Which she removed to close the shutters. Aren't Edinburgh apartments marvellous? At the end of the day. Not this day. Only the word. Say it again. Lips and eyes closed. Eidolon.

Don't even go there. Let the barman preside like a little god. A little arse-faced god. Drying out a glass with a damp dishtowel. None to spoil their perfect day. This isn't that. And bound to be new after thirteen years. And so she is. White blouse, black skirt. Looking a little puzzled. No, puzzlement gone now. Looking a little efficient. Can she see him as he nears? She doesn't look up. Till he is bang beside her. Smiles. Faintly. A pale ale, please.

What is at stake here? A couple in another corner eating

their crisps. The bag open to both like a burst belly. Licking their fingers intermittently. They touch the same crisp and laugh, then resume. If there is conversation he cannot hear it. Bikers by the look of things. Which is the more enamoured? Impossible to say. A perfect equanimity of indolence and silence, who could ask for more? She finishes her drink. Then he. They get up to go, jackets swung round, helmets underarm. They will follow each other as they go, she in the lead, then he. Stop off in another place with nobody watching. As lovingly.

Well, this is different too. Not looking on from a ledge in air or muck slope. Seems to have free run of the place. Free rein. To loiter, to walk. And if he meets himself? There is no self to meet. Out in the back they are stacking. In a corner a man alone, pretending to read. Bury My Heart at Wounded Knee. Pint and a packet of Kensitas. Barbour jacket. He will go out for a smoke soon. Could he take his place? Assume anew? This must be the place of hope after all. Before nothing. Not a feathered thing. A pub in the Cowgate.

No ashtrays, so that is different. The Smoking, Health and Social Care (Scotland) Act. Disinfect the air, that's the idea. They puffed away like mad. The smokers outside at the picnic tables. Only, he doesn't venture out. It's not possible she will be there. In truth he cannot bear to look. So why come? Because he said he would. Is there a hint of a thrill in his being here? The widow's self-preening on the morning of the funeral? The dying man's self-regard? Then he would look. The thrill is all in the garden. Where they puffed away, legs intertwined like the surface roots. All muck and beerspill. A pane of glass in the swing door if he can bear to look. Misted and scratched. Just visible in the bar mirror,

tilted to look down on us. Christ of St John of the Cross.
He cannot.

The grand hearth. Not currently in use. Standing willowy at
it, an elbow propped. Upwards. He could be the master of all
he surveys. How nice to say so. I am the master now, says the
man hurtling to his. God knows, ridiculous. He looked so
on his honeymoon, remember that one? Elbows up. Elbows
down. He stares into it. What a dark hole to disappear into.
Not swept out sufficiently. He could crouch at it and call up.
Scare the crows. Willowy in a field. The sun searing.

Turn on a sixpence. As she always could. Swift depart, from
where she hadn't been. Leaving him as before, as he had
never been. Good to get that over with. Begin again. Start
the slide again. Will he see her in another place? It would
be good if he could get there. He doesn't seem to be able to
direct. He will fix his eyes in front, a foot from his feet. Watch
for the ground to give. Nothing seems to be happening.
Hold on. Here we go. If he could thank somebody quickly
now he would. In spite of all. The deadness and not seeing
her. For letting him be here.

In the appointed place. At the appointed time.

25

- I haven't seen you like this since our wedding day. You're shaking like an aspen tree.

  - I know. I can't help it.

  - What is it?

  - I don't know. I've done trips like this a thousand times.

  - I've never known you to be afraid of flying.

  - It's not that.

  - What? You're making me nervous too.

  - Just the feeling something awful is going to happen.

  - Who to? You?

  - Me. You. Us.

  - You don't have to worry on that front. Though it's sweet that you do.

  - This doesn't feel sweet.

  - Come here.

  - Thanks.

  - I've a valium if you need it.

  - You have valium?

  - Just for emergencies.

  - I think this is one.

Those books that told him of the non-existence of time, what a time they took to read! A year out of his life at least. He who can afford to squander none. Salute them as they pass, finite now, filing like metal birds. That is too much. Like the little soldiers on his toy drum. Now we are talking! If he gets that far back he will be nearly there. Bonjour, monsieur. No time to babble now. Straight as the arrow, and the arrow slicing that. Zeno of Elea, old fraud, keep out of this. Or young fraud, was it? Bit late to check. My arrow will hit the target as it is myself. And well you knew it. There is no stasis in space, no silence in the chamber. Oh joy – Hallo, sir – if he gets that far. If he gets that far he will have conquered space, time, and all creation.

He will not meet her here.

In haste. All correspondence signed off this way. He who never hurried in his puff. Until now, when no effort is required. Velocity of a falling body, tell it to the birds. Speak soon another, but reserved for electronic mail, as he insists on calling it. As if a matter of pride. As if there were something to be kept up. In haste when once with love. That's not right. He never loved in business. Where business is, there love cannot be. But even his love letters now, when there are none. Missives to Rosemary. In haste. She teases him about it, naturally. But he is undeterred. My love, I took some brickbats for your sake, but that was in another country. He is lonely at the club. Even a decade ago some in business had read a book. But he is never at the club. The club, for him, does not exist. And if it did, he wouldn't let it let him in. At least not up to his waist. Ha, yes, the Groucho. It all coheres, in haste, that's the surprise. Or would be, if anything could. Such as a body passing him in air.

- We have to get more hands on deck.

- Then call the agency. You know you have my permission.

- Not another temp, an employee.

- It isn't the right time.

- When we're snowed under? Should we wait till it's quiet again?

- It soon might be.

- Don't be so bloody crabbit.

- Don't be so bloody wasteful.

- Oh go and play with the traffic.

- You're lucky I'm a tolerant employer.

- Employ me or not. I've been here from the off, I know where the bodies are buried.

- Haha.

- Seriously, we need someone who knows her stuff.

- A good temp should know her stuff.

- A good temp is hard to find.

- Then find her.

On a sunlit Saturday. Where has he heard that before? These random phrases. *Randomness isn't freedom. Who would value being random?* That one he knows. Karl Popper, was it? Or some physicist? A long time since he read those boys. The thrill he used to feel! He is allowed such thoughts. Better than sex, he once said. Not sex with me, the girl said, and loosened his belt. *The universe is a carpet of undulating foam.* No it isn't. But it was. Are we there yet? That must be the Forth Bridge. The rail, not the road. Though it is the road he sees. Through the crossing cantilever arms. That's it! A wedding seen from a train, just as in the book he put down, capital–lambda–shaped over his crotch, hiding his mild erection. On a sunlit Saturday.

Invigorating in the sun. The old walled garden. It could almost be like they planned it, if he closed his eyes. Are his eyes closed? Impossible to tell at speed. But when the sun goes, ruinous. Of course there are the neighbours. They were there then too, hands gripping mugs with matching hope. These trees bushes. That bush twigs. It was a jolly hot summer, all told. Queues at the pumps. A hosepipe ban, perhaps. He is allowed such thoughts. Now, no dearth of water. But not today. A fine day to stand in the garden and recall old hopes. With hands clean and belly full. The slightly fishy ham repeating. Are they ended? Look at the climbers and creepers.

- Now would be a good time to sell. This is the peak, believe me.

- But I don't. You said the same last month, and look what's happened.

- It's time to downsize anyway.

- We can't. Marianne's still here.

- When did you last see her?

- She'll be back when the boyfriend lets her down.

- He seems keen on her.

- You don't pick up on the half of it. Is the business in difficulty?

- No.

- Well, then.

- But it soon might be. The world's accelerating into a brick wall.

- Not our wall.

- I wouldn't bet on it.

A wasp's would be sharper. Like that time running home from school. No, a bee, a bee, crushed under his bended knee. Between thigh and calf, a region, he has forgotten the word. If he ever knew it. He is allowed such thoughts. A pity to waste them so soon, though. He searches the carpet for an answer. The little bugger. Same shade as it. A sort of tawny millipede. Or they all are. Serves him right for prying. Checking was she asleep. He will go through her purse another time. No he won't. He will never feel the urge again. It is over. That part, at least. Who can tell what's in store? A crushed bee's last thought. Popliteal.

- Is this yours?

   - Yes, it is. Thanks.

   - It rolled under your seat.

   - Yes. It must have fallen. Thanks.

   - Are you who I think you are?

   - Almost certainly not.

Blood a sure sign. Rushing to his face at the slightest prompting. Just like when he was a boy. Remember that grief? Flushing with every passing stranger on the walk to school. He is allowed these thoughts. But different now. A glass of wine now. Or just cooking, when more than one pan is on the stove. Is that word allowed? It's because he holds his breath in the kitchen, Rosemary says. And in bed, asleep.

   - You have sleep apnea.

   - No, I just snore.

   - It doesn't bother me, I'm used to it. I ought to be after twenty-four years.

   - Twenty-two.

– So few already?

But the blood. Mounting up. He feels it. Ready to gush. In an instant. Spraying the spectators. His bowed bloody head. That would be something. On the commentator's clean white shirt.

A new module on the crash. Who could he get to write that?

– Why not you?

– Be serious.

– You predicted it. Not many did.

– So?

– So you can draw on foresight as well as hindsight. Anyone else would have to work backwards from the fact.

– Which is the proper way to write a scholarly text. No, give this one to Petra.

– Petra?

– Have you seen her reverse into a parking space? She does it to perfection every time.

– I can't ask Petra.

– Why not?

– She left a month ago.

In the office he left he is back. A message to come in.

– The figures a problem?

– Not really.

– What, then?

– Just these expenses. Hotel bills. They are in your name, but they don't match your other expenses. You can't have been in two places at once.

- You called me in for *that*?

- It's trifling, but we can't ignore it.

- Let me see. I see.

- What should I do?

- Leave out any bills for the Shalimar. I wasn't there.

Backstreet hurdy gurdy. In the pouring rain. He is not now and never has been an artist.

- You have the talent. Remember how you drew for Roger?

- Not Marianne?

- No, not so much. You were busier then.

- They were just doodles.

- Oh I don't know. I couldn't have done them. And I did try.

- Did you?

- Yes, once you'd left the room. I am full of surprises.

- Don't I know.

- What do you mean? What exactly do you mean?

- Just that. That I know you.

- I don't know that you do.

Dear God, not again.

This is the best thing I've ever done. This. This falling now.

26

On a striped deckchair at last. In the back garden at last. With the startled dog muzzled at last. And a beer poured to perfection at last. And the hum of the lawnmowers diminished at last. And the neighbour's bin collected at last. And the Dance of the Sugar Plum Fairy ending at last. And only the thought of his father at last.

It is enough.

It is not enough.

In a frame above his attic desk. Not directly in front, that would be too much. Enough to glance at, for approval. Did I do OK, Dad? Far enough aside to avoid if he had done wrong. Or was doing wrong. Have I done wrong? No, not that, never said that except in jest. To the children. Too soon to name them in this fog, if it is a fog. Attack! The rifle almost as tall, with its bayonet. Could Dad have been small? Perspective and respect say no. Respect for Da another quip to the kids. All from films. Matinee movie time. Respect for moi, the boy says. Too soon? Soon and for the rest of your life. Take it down.

I loved you.

Turning her back on him, saying if he thought so, then of course he must.

    – I do think so. I don't think she's crying wolf this time.

    – Well, you said it.

    – Rosemary, be fair.

    – I am being fair, dear. See how fair I am being.

    – I just want to check. I'll know straight away.

    – You can't tell on the phone?

    – You know me. I'm not good on the phone.

    – Well that's true.

    – I could be there and back in a day.

    – No need for that. If you go, you'd better stay.

    – What will you do?

    – Without you? I will perish in an instant.

    – Come with me.

    – You are joking.

    – Can I say I am? Even though I'm not?

    – That seems to be the theme for the day.

The old number on speed dial in his head. The old domain. Only, they added a new digit. A second two. Two twos, twenty-two. Two little ducks, quack quack quack. She taught him that. Tuesday night was bingo night, chips for them both if she won. Chips for a line or for two lines. Never was a full house. Is that allowed here? He says aloud, Is that allowed here? Memory inside memory. Apparently so. But three into two won't go. Three quacks into two ducks won't go. Same for eyes. Shut her wild, wild eyes with kisses three. Wouldn't you go back to the lesser kissed eye and kiss that again. Kiss them both once again. Two times three is satisfactory. To him, perhaps. Not to wild-eyed her.

- A fern cake and a Paris bun, please.

    - Are you back for a visit?

    - Is that you, Frances?

    - Who else?

    - How long have you been working here now?

    - Too long.

    - It seems like only yesterday I was coming in here with my mum.

    - For a fern cake and a Paris bun. I know.

    - So predictable?

    - Ach, it's all right, son. People don't change. Not around here.

    - Is the library still upstairs?

    - You remember it? That's right, you used to pop in here afterwards. You looked so serious with your little books. I see you've done well for yourself.

    - I don't know about that.

    - Son, take a compliment when it's offered.

    - Sorry. Thanks.

    - Is that everything?

    - That's all for now. You're looking well, Frances.

    - Away with you, you didn't even know me.

    - Take a compliment.

    - Haha. Give my regards to your mum.

- Nice of you to call.

    - I was passing.

    - Passing? Where?

    - Oh, nowhere. Past the old domain.

- Do you like the new fireplace?

- The fire's gone.

- It was a dirty old thing. Do you like the tiles?

- Yes. Nice and smooth.

- Aren't they? Why did you call?

- I was just passing.

- Have you had a row with Rosemary?

- No. Yes.

- It's not too late to move back, son.

- Yes. Yes it is.

The masticating jaws. That is a picture now! And the crumbs they let fall, pushed by a finger to the side of the plate. Perhaps to be scooped up later. Pinched between forefinger and thumb. A pincushion, that one. And the nose going the same way. Horrible thought. But a picture all the same. If he hangs around long enough he will find out. About the crumbs. There doesn't appear to be any ground to fall from, and yet the crumbs fall. A different gravity, perhaps. If not 32 feet per sec per sec, then what? With no distant celestial object to aid measurement, he hazards a guess.

The crumbs fall at a speed she determines.

As good as any.

She saw her father last night. No, not in a dream, walking out of the sliding-door cupboard. He looked disappointed. She didn't like to see that look on his face.

- Mum?

- Son.

- You all right here by yourself?

- But I'm not by myself.

- Grandfather doesn't count.

- He does, you know.

- If you've not got it, don't flaunt it.

- Yes, that was one of his sayings.

- Evil is as good doesn't.

- I don't remember that one.

- You'll scratch your bare arse yet.

- No. That was mine.

War time was whore time. His dad said that. With a glance out the room, when she was out the room. Especially on armistice day. He remembers now. With the picture of his dad in uniform in his hand he remembers now. That crooked smile. A good crooked. His own teeth, too, but bearing the scars. Of a life of sucked sugar-stick. We were the first to arrive, he would say. Strolling through fields of barley. The villagers on high alert. Go back to your Glasgow slums. I'll have you know I'm not Glasgow, he told them. I am Glasgow *overspill*.

Incipient dementia. Just as he suspected.

- How will I tell her?

- Oh, no need for that.

- Aren't you meant to these days?

- Certainly, if she asks outright.

- And you think she won't?

- I haven't scheduled an appointment.

- I see. So what do I do?

- Carry on as per. If she deteriorates rapidly you might want to think about a home. Or get someone in.

- Right. She's started having visions of her father.

- Is this a source of distress?

- No. I think she's glad of the company.

- Well, then.

Why only voices now? Same inchoate dark as when drifting off to sleep. Yet how far from sleep this is! And the voices sudden, too. And loud. Too, too loud. Turn it down down there! Down there is voiceless existlessness, here there is – what? Not a patch of ground at all. A black cloud. Oh that is too good. He is in his black cloud at last. Such as threatened to engulf him all his days.

- You always miss the main event. Your mind is always on some sideshow.

He eyes her slantwise, as she (of necessity) eyes him.

- I'm your mother, I should know.

They are in the fruit and veg aisle of a Safeway supermarket after mass. His mouth still rasping from the wafer.

- Mum, she is *not*. OK?

- Then why's she all dolled up all of a sudden?

- Says who?

- And why's the phone always engaged when you're not there?

- Why are you ringing if I'm not there?

- Somebody has to look out for you. If not me, who?

- I can look out for myself.

- That you cannot do.

27

In the rockery near the palace it begins. Preceded by umpteen loaded glances. In the office, the lift, the lobby. In the rockery she scuffs her shoe and licks her finger, spreading saliva over the scuff. But so shapely as she does so! Like a swan regarding something to its rear. This could be said better, no matter. Green cardigan, grey skirt, brown shoes. A smudge of dirt on her fingertip, removed in an instant. How she got that spit into the hankie so quickly he will never know. A woman is a wonder. Any woman. No, not any. Regard only this one now. So elegant and interested among the tree ferns. Asking him to say the Latin names. Seeming to delight in them. Cyathea medullaris. Blechnum gibbum.

Could be the heat, perhaps. Strolling like royal walkers through the hothouse, he a step behind, so that a deliberate halt will take him into her. It does and she straightens up, lets him linger there.

He will take her trailing hand as they leave.

Calculate incalculable loss. Subtract the nourishment loss gave.

He writes this out on his deskpad. The sum, not the words. Not the sum, a doodle. Like the number 8 on its side. Spirograph. He was always good at art. His mother said he was always good at art. A hobby, not a career.

The sideways 8 is lashed and tied like Gulliver. It is a story he read as a boy.

But only the beginning. He never ventured further than the beginning.

Why is love so strong in the beginning? And after the end?

He calculates again, even through lunch.

The figure stays the same.

First vacancy on the left. Is that right? A veritable slip of a girl, asking directions. Odd place to ask. Odd time, the office world shutting up shop. He holds one of the lift doors and it jerks back, though she isn't getting in here. She is on the right floor already. Nevertheless she puts a foot across the threshold, the wiring in her brain responding to his courtesy.

She is not the main show though. Not by a long chalk. The main show is downstairs waiting for him in the lobby, bolder now. Inspecting flyers, one leg crossed behind the other. Oh Eleanor.

- It's been a month we've been together now, she says.

- Let's celebrate, he says. However you like.

- Dinner at the Chip?

- Good call.

And so they dine at the Chip, and after repair to hers. A smart room in a West End flat.

They make love as month-young lovers do, with vigour and panache. Only, at the moment of climax, his attention shifts. He sees again the pale slim face of the girl he misdirected.

She is in a plastic mac in the rain. She, Rosemary. He behind mad wipers. She in the passenger seat, reclining. She, Eleanor. Except she sits up suddenly at sight of her. And then the seat shoots up. What a fright she gets! She, Eleanor.

- Do you think she saw?

- Couldn't possibly have.

- I think I caught her eye.

- That's an illusion.

- An illusion?

- Like being in a dark room looking out at people in the street. You see them clearly, they don't see you, but you think they do.

- It isn't dark in here.

- It is with the rain.

- That's right. The rain.

- So you see, we're perfectly safe.

- But the car!

- What?

- She surely knows your car.

- She wouldn't even know the reg.

- Right.

- Can you pass the CD?

- Hold on. I can put it in.

- Thanks.

- I think she saw.

A movement towards and he slips. Oh hell. Silt first. It is all crumbling away. What is all crumbling away? The rock he reposes on. What? Which?

No, he is not dislodged as yet. His footing secure. His

foot. In a kind of sandshoe. Well, that is different. Where is he now?

He is on a road to nowhere. Ha! Say again. He is on the long path of Fala Moor. With a friend, with the one true friend he ever had. Knapsacks on their backs. For their already eaten sandwiches. Cider for the sun.

– I am in love again.

– Who with?

– A temp from the agency.

– Is she nice?

– Looking, you mean?

– That too.

– Yes, that too.

– Rosemary know?

– I don't see how.

– One never does. But they do.

– Have some grapes, at least.

– I ate already, she says.

– Didn't I say I would make lunch?

– Did you? What difference does it make?

– I went to a lot of trouble.

– On my account?

– Yes!

Her shielded eyes regard him. Other hand as if trailing in water. The dark sparkles.

– Then let me see what you've got.

The desk not in disarray. This they would find alarming. All of the correspondence up to date. Up to yesterday's date, whatever that was. Oh look, he is forgetting already. Continuously in the present now. This must be the first symptom. Well, that isn't so bad, is it? Forgetfulness is like, is like … Yet he can still see the date's font on his desk, the different sizes. The number large and black. The month above, smaller and black. The day above that, smaller still and white. What was the name of the day? Ah yes, he sees it. Friday! Or possibly Thursday! Or possibly Wednesday! Or possibly Tuesday! Or possibly Monday! A leap is a backwards step, after all. Before nothing. Like a diver. Showboating, if that's the word. It isn't.

- You're getting thin, said Rosemary. You've been taking care of yourself lately. I hope you're not having an affair.

She rolled over, towards the glass of water on the bedside cabinet.

- I don't mind, she said. In fact I quite like it.

She liked his look or his having an affair? Or the thought of the possibility of his having an affair, now he was slimmer?

The electric eel that had slithered down his spine was transformed into the kipper tie being crossed and knotted by his huge hands. His hands that felt huge in that moment, with their seaweed-like throbbing veins.

- You might want to think about your attire too, she said.

What was this? The old vertigo? Another ledge? But the air was clear blue between the ground and the roof.

It wasn't another ledge it was a branch.

It wasn't a branch it was a tentacle.

It wasn't a tentacle it was a thick stipe of seaweed drying in the sun.

Eleanor was there, spread-eagled on a second rock, just as she had been when he had lifted the stipe and aimlessly let it drop, except seen from a different angle. An angle from which he, too, could now be seen. He had only fleetingly caught sight of himself from the back before. But the wonder of it could not make him take his eyes off of *her*. She was spread-eagled on the rock with one arm suspended in air and the other shielding her eyes. Her skirt riding up a little. Below her, on a blanket on the sand, the remnants of their lunch – the lunch he had made that morning without arousing suspicion, and she had barely touched.

Down and down and down and down and

To act on a suicidal impulse, he had the genius idea of leading with his left foot, thus confusing the wiring in his brain for the split second needed to complete the leap.

The first time was on a diseased elm near some lock-ups. His two friends had already jumped and were below, shouting up at him, demanding that he jump. After about a minute he did. He never forgot that minute and never again placed himself in a position to experience another like it.

Until now.

Until then.

A note would have been too much.

He would be leaving behind a business that was still solvent despite the crash, a mother who could see out of the sides of her eyes only, a wife of twenty-four years, a mistress of several months, and a son and a daughter he had never before amazed. The coroner would label his suicide 'death by misadventure'. The insurance company would pay up.

The crash a possible motive in others' eyes, despite the company's solvency. Those he left behind could console themselves by blaming the world's bankers and speculators. They would not blame themselves, though they would sometimes say that they did. Not the son or daughter.

This is the story of a fall. It won't take a minute.

A secretary two floors below, the window behind her head open a crack. She would be eating lightly buttered rye bread. This is what she always did at that time.

Would she think it was the cry of a bird?

Martin Prendergast did not care if anybody heard or did not hear his cry. He did not mean to cry out. But he heard his own cry. It was the most natural thing in the world.

Where was he now?